D1642196

PSYCHIATRY, EDUCATION, AND THE YOUNG ADULT

PSYCHIATRY, EDUCATION, AND THE YOUNG ADULT

By

DANA L. FARNSWORTH, M.D.

Henry K. Oliver Professor of Hygiene
Director, University Health Services
Harvard University
Cambridge, Massachusetts

With a Foreword by

Francis J. Braceland, M.D.

CHARLES C THOMAS • **PUBLISHER**
Springfield • *Illinois* • *U.S.A.*

Published and Distributed Throughout the World by

CHARLES C THOMAS • PUBLISHER

BANNERSTONE HOUSE

301-327 East Lawrence Avenue, Springfield, Illinois, U.S.A.

NATCHEZ PLANTATION HOUSE

735 North Atlantic Boulevard, Fort Lauderdale, Florida, U.S.A.

With THOMAS BOOKS careful attention is given to all details of manufacturing and design. It is the Publisher's desire to present books that are satisfactory as to their physical qualities and artistic possibilities and appropriate for their particular use. THOMAS BOOKS will be true to those laws of quality that assure a good name and good will.

Printed in the United States of America

W-2

FOREWORD

*When we are out of sympathy with the young, I think
our work in this world is over.*
GEORGE MACDONALD

ONE CAN ASSURE Dr. MacDonald in his particular place in
heaven that neither parents nor educators are really out of
sympathy with the young but they are having a hard time trying
to understand just what it is they want and what they are about.
Young folks are disquieted, as they have been throughout the
course of history, but present day unrest seems to be greater
and seems to become manifest at an earlier age. Their circumstances are different, less is demanded of them, they have more
money, and they are more mobile. They are more vocal and
more demonstrative when things displease them and, while some
of their unrest is healthy, some of it is self-defeating. Be that as
it may, they take their problems to college with them and sometimes into early matrimony.

The author of this present volume has spent his professional
life working with these young people in educational settings and
making efforts to understand and assist them and to teach and
enthuse others about that art. This presentation is evidence
that he does both particularly well.

When the Salmon Committee of The New York Academy
of Medicine, which sponsors the nation's annual prize psychiatric lectureship, decided that the important subject which
faced psychiatry, and indeed faced the country at large, was the
mental health of our college students, that subject was chosen as
the 1964 lecture topic. The heritage of this lectureship is an
enviable one, for men of the calibre of Adolph Meyer, A. A.
Brill, Horace Magoun, René DuBos, and other notables have
graced its roster.

Once the 1964 subject was decided upon, the choice of a lecturer posed no problem. The Committee unanimously turned to Dr. Dana Farnsworth. Not only had he three decades of experience in psychiatry in educational settings, with a wartime interlude in which he distinguished himself, but also he is the outstanding man in his field. Highly respected by his professional brethren, he is also highly regarded and his opinions are sought by some of the country's top educators. That his choice as Salmon Lecturer was a happy one is now common knowledge and this present outstanding work is an expanded version of those lectures.

Apparently, the subject matter was even more timely than at first was supposed. The unrest in college students is chronicled almost daily in the various communications media. Only a decade ago we were complaining about the apathy of our students but now the pendulum has swung and, in view of the fact that the population of our educational institutions bids fair to increase over the next few years, the need for understanding and expert handling of the emotional problems which the students present becomes even more pressing.

New federal statistics on college enrollments indicate that in the Fall of 1965, 5.9 million students were enrolled in our colleges and universities, 68 per cent of them in publicly controlled institutions. This represents an increase in the student body of 14.5 per cent over the 1964 enrollment. The population of private institutions increased 7.8 per cent over the same period. At present there is no sign of a let-up in the demand for college admission and there seems to be no promise of one in the near future.

In that it is to the college group that the nation will look for its future leaders, several statements made by the distinguished author of this book give us pause. From those relatively few institutions which have comprehensive mental health services, he says, a number of estimates of clinical problems can be made. For every 10,000 students, 1,000 will have emotional conflicts of sufficient severity to warrant professional help. Three to four hundred will have feelings of depression severe enough to impair their efficiency and, even more distressing, of the five to twenty who will attempt suicide one to three will succeed. Fifteen to twenty will become ill enough to require treatment in mental hospitals.

It is not my function here to paraphrase the author's findings or even to repeat many of his statements which impress me mightily, but there are some things which should be emphasized. First, the book breathes hope and gives promise of understanding and assistance. There is nothing lugubrious about it. For instance, of those who leave college because of emotional and mental illness a considerable number return and are graduated. *Some of the most capable students are in this group and the favorable prognosis of those who receive good treatment suggests that colleges cannot ignore their problems.*

Next, the reader is surprised to learn that many colleges do little about these situations "because of lack of awareness of what is happening, for lack of money or professional resources, or because their administrators do not consider these problems a proper concern for educators." One wonders how this latter group arrives at its conclusions and wonders too what is said to students and their parents when one of their number has to be sent home because of emotional upset. Is he then discarded and forever looked upon with suspicion? Or does he have to develop psychosomatic disorder in order to attain an aura of respectability? The fact that some superior students have upsets which prove to be only temporary should give these educators pause for thought.

This work is practical in all respects. It answers numerous questions which trouble parents and discusses the varied emotional problems which plague teachers and administrators. The role of the counselor is outlined; counseling by faculty members is put in proper perspective. Sensible insight into the causes of student rootlessness and restlessness is given and all of the discussion is free from technical jargon.

Identity crises, dropouts, drugs, and that dilemma not only of the colleges but of the age, sexual morality, all are frankly discussed, as are the various emotional problems which plague administrators and attract newspaper columnists and commentators. All of these situations are considered with an understanding and a reasonableness that could only be born of long professional experience and a practical knowledge of the difficulties inherent in the conduct of educational institutions.

The author is of the opinion that a great majority of psychological problems encountered in college have their origin in interpersonal relations occurring before the student enters an educational institution, rather than arising *de novo* in the new college environment. Hard work is rarely a cause of emotional disturbance unless the intellectual potential is not up to it.

A statement made by one of Dr. Farnsworth's colleagues seems especially apt as far as the reason for making psychiatric help available to college students is concerned. The statement was made by Harvard's Dean of Freshmen, Dr. F. S. von Stade, Jr.: "When so many capable youngsters are on the beach it makes good sense to have expert lifeguards when some of them go beyond their depth." There is a great deal of wisdom in that observation.

Well, it is apparent from the tone of this foreword that its writer is well persuaded of the excellence of this book. It should be read not only by teachers and college officials, but also by physicians, psychiatrists, and educated laymen, in fact by anyone who has the privilege of dealing with young adults. It is a definitive work, the best exposition of psychiatry in a college setting yet to appear, and it is all done so beautifully and so comfortably that it will be considered and discussed for a long time to come.

FRANCIS J. BRACELAND, M.D.

Chairman, The Salmon Committee on
Psychiatry and Mental Hygiene
The New York Academy of Medicine

PREFACE

THIS BOOK REPRESENTS an attempt to describe some of the advantages to be derived from that collaboration of educators and psychiatrists in colleges and universities whose goal is to free their students' minds from the handicaps of ignorance, crippling conflict, and lack of vision of what they may become. Conditions are changing rapidly, however, and with them the nature of the stresses which students undergo. Some students can deal with stress adequately and constructively. Those who cannot are not our weakest or poorest students; in fact, they are some of our most creative individuals.

Students with good minds, but who carry a too-heavy burden of emotional conflict, warrant the best help we can provide, particularly in the initial stages of their difficulties when therapeutic intervention is most effective. Quandaries which, if unresolved, may lead to permanent handicaps, are of chief concern. Psychiatrists believe that their experience in concentrated study and treatment of those in whom stress has become distress is of value in the educational experience of all students. Their efforts in the last half-century in a few institutions suggest that when they work closely with students, teachers, other types of counselors, and community agencies the intellectual standards of the institutions go up, not down; understanding is not soft-headedness. Attention to mental health is not diversionary; it lies at the heart of the educational process, freeing the individual to use his best efforts even while enjoying and wanting to do so.

In this book, the terms psychiatry and psychiatric service are usually used in such a manner that their meaning is unmistakable. At times, however, it is more convenient to use them to include the activities of psychiatrists, psychiatric social workers, and clinical psychologists combined. In many psychiatric services psychiatrists are in a minority, and in most services of the future this will be the usual arrangement, unless many more physicians specialize in psychiatry than are now doing so. Although psychiatrists have the broad range of training and experience that should ideally fit them to do the best work of any present discipline concerned with counseling, they are not necessarily the most capable. The individual's capabilities are more important than his belonging to a particular discipline. In short, a good psychiatric social worker or clinical psychologist can do a better job directing a "psychiatric service" than a poor psychiatrist, though they must have genuine medical collaboration (at least) if the best interests of their clients (patients) are to be safeguarded.

This book is directed to educators of all types, whether they call themselves administrators, teachers, clinical psychologists, or counselors. Psychiatrists will be interested in how their specialty may be used in a setting far different from the mental hospital; it is hoped that they will see that hospitals have much to learn by adapting educational practices to the task of treating their patients, just as schools and colleges can provide better education when the feelings and emotions of their students are considered and understood. Educational psychiatry is a young subspecialty; this volume is designed to hasten its development.

ACKNOWLEDGMENTS

I wish to express my indebtedness to the Thomas W. Salmon Committee of the New York Academy of Medicine and particularly its Chairman, Dr. Francis J. Braceland, for stimulating the production of this book by selecting me to give the Salmon Lectures in Psychiatry in 1964.

To my colleagues of the Harvard University Health Services I owe warm thanks for their help in making the ideas in this book represent as accurately as possible the actual conditions of practice. Special gratitude is due Doctors Henry H. Babcock, Graham B. Blaine, Jr., Leo J. Cass, Stanley H. King, Preston K. Munter, Armand M. Nicholi, Jr., Douglas H. Powell, Irvin Taube, Paul A. Walters, Jr., Joseph L. Zerman and Mrs. Lida R. Carmen.

To Sister Thomas Aquinas, R.S.M., and Sister Mary Louise, R.S.M., for permission to use material in a lecture on "Insight and Choice—The College Student's Opportunity" given at Mt. Mercy College, Pittsburgh, Pennsylvania, on October 26, 1964.

To Dr. Joseph K. Stewart, President of West Virginia Academy of Science, for permission to use material in a lecture on "Student Revolt: Origin and Consequences" given at the 40th Annual Meeting of the West Virginia Academy of Science at Fairmont, West Virginia, on April 24, 1965.

To Mr. G. Kerry Smith, Executive Secretary of the Association for Higher Education, for permission to use material in a lecture on "Student Restlessness and Rootlessness: Is There An Answer?" given at the National Education Association Convention in New York City on June 28, 1965.

To Mr. John J. Wittich, Executive Director of the College Student Personnel Institute, for permission to use material in a lecture on "Helping Students Live with Their Tensions—and

Like It" given at the Annual Conference of the College Student Personnel Institute in Claremont, California, November 2, 1965.

To Dr. Earl J. McGrath of the Institute for Higher Education of Teachers College, Columbia University, for permission to use material from an address on "The Liberal Arts College's Responsibility for the Emotional Stability of Students" given at the Meeting of Liberal Arts College Presidents, December 5, 1965.

To the School of Medicine's Department of Psychiatry of the State University of New York at Buffalo for permission to use material from a lecture on "Unrest in the Colleges" given on February 3, 1966.

Mr. James L. Trawick, Director, Division of Consumer Education and Voluntary Compliance, Food and Drug Administration, Department of Health, Education, and Welfare, as well as Dr. Norman N. Alberstadt, and Mr. Lewis P. Lasher of this agency kindly reviewed the chapter on Drugs.

For the editorial assistance of Mary Claire Adams and Helen S. Chasin I wish to express my sincere appreciation. The painstaking care which Elaine Colebrook, Sarah M. MacLeod, Ruth R. Simonds, and other members of the staff of the University Health Services applied to the preparation of this book is only another example of their constant devotion to their work.

My special thanks are due Rev. Theodore Hesburgh, C.S.C., President of the University of Notre Dame, for permission to use a lecture which was given on May 4, 1964, as part of a *Symposium on The Person in the Contemporary World* in connection with the dedication of the new Notre Dame Library; to the *American Journal of Orthopsychiatry* for permission to use material on sexual morality published in the July 1965 issue under the same title as Chapter IX of this book; to Dr. John H. Talbot, Editor of the *Journal of the American Medical Association*, for permission to use portions of an editorial on hallucinogenic drugs published September 14, 1963; to Father G. Gordon Henderson of Wheeling College, West Virginia, for permission to use material on developmental tasks of college students first prepared for use in the Jesuit Educational Workshop for Jesuit Student Personnel Programs and Services, held at Regis College, Denver, Colorado,

July 18 to 30, 1965; to Father William F. Troy, President of Wheeling College, for permission to adapt the contents of The Muldowney Memorial Lecture at Wheeling College on March 30, 1966 for use in the chapter on Preventive Psychiatry.

D. L. F.

The Thomas William Salmon Memorial Lectures

The Salmon Lectures of the New York Academy of Medicine were established in 1931 as a memorial to Thomas William Salmon, M.D. and for the advancement of the objectives to which his professional career had been wholly devoted.

Dr. Salmon died in 1927, at the age of 51, after a career of extraordinary service in psychiatric practice and education and in the development of a world-wide movement for the better treatment and prevention of mental disorders and for the promotion of mental health.

Following his death, a group of his many friends organized a committee for the purpose of establishing one or more memorials that might serve to preserve and pass on to future generations some of the spirit and purpose of his supremely noble and useful life. Five hundred and ninety-six subscriptions were received, three hundred and nineteen from physicians.

For the purpose of giving lasting quality to the lectures as a memorial to Dr. Salmon and of extending their usefulness, it was stipulated that the lectures should each be published in a bound volume. This volume is one of that series.

The Salmon Committee is composed of the following members:

FRANCIS J. BRACELAND, M.D., Chairman
KENNETH E. APPEL, M.D.
LAWRENCE C. KOLB, M.D.
DAVID M. LEVY, M.D.
NOLAN D. C. LEWIS, M.D.
WILLIAM T. LHAMON, M.D.
H. HOUSTON MERRITT, M.D.
S. BERNARD WORTIS, M.D.

Ex Officio

HOWARD REID CRAIG, M.D.
HAROLD BROWN KEYES, M.D.

CONTENTS

PSYCHIATRY, EDUCATION, AND THE YOUNG ADULT

CHAPTER I

PSYCHIATRY'S ROLE IN HIGHER EDUCATION

A FEW PSYCHIATRISTS have been interested in the special challenges posed by college students and their quandaries for several decades. Stewart Paton at Princeton (1910), Smiley Blanton at the University of Wisconsin (1914), Karl Menninger at Washburne College (1920), Arthur Ruggles at Dartmouth and Yale (1921, 1925), and Austen Fox Riggs at Vassar (1923) were among the first psychiatrists to appreciate the possibilities for prevention of crippling emotional conflict among students by working on the causes of distress with both students and faculty members rather than waiting for the classic syndromes of illness to appear.* It now seems evident that these early workers were thinking along the same lines as do those who are now furthering the principles collectively known as community or social psychiatry.

In 1926, Yale University, with the aid of the Commonwealth Fund, set up a five-year program for the development of mental hygiene and psychiatry. The basic intent was to develop an efficient student psychiatric service and to study the university and its life. The psychiatrists who inaugurated the service were Stewart Paton, Harry Kerns, Lloyd Thompson, and Clements Fry. They thought that as college psychiatrists they should know the university community and be known by it. They considered knowledge of the college environment essential to the understanding of the individual student in conflict. Following this

---

* A more detailed account of the early college psychiatric services may be found in my earlier volume on Mental Health in College and University (Harvard University Press, 1957).

3

initial period, Dr. Fry became chief of the service and carried on its activities with superlative skill until his death in 1955. Not only was he one of Yale's most beloved figures but he was also the first "career man" in college psychiatry, the person who has set standards and pointed out directions of future growth to all who have followed him. Those of us now in college psychiatry owe far more than is generally realized to the principles enunciated by Dr. Fry.

Since World War II, the growing interest in higher education generally has been accompanied by many evidences of concern with the emotional status of individual students. Administrators and parents have always been aware that students have problems, but until the last few decades there have been few effective methods for understanding the nature, diversity, and extent of their troubles. Newspapers and magazines are now becoming interested in these quandaries and their effects, as if something new had been injected into the processes of higher education. Opinion seems to be growing that college students of today are suffering more than their predecessors from emotional disorders, that they are filled with resentment toward their elders and toward society generally, and that the colleges must do something about the situation.

There is no convincing evidence that students of today are any more subject to emotional distress than in times past, mainly because there are no reliable surveys of such disorders in past decades. It does appear certain that both teachers and students are more inclined to think in psychological terms than formerly. As a result, recognition of students' difficulties is now quite general. There is also a much larger proportion of persons between eighteen and twenty-five in college or university than formerly and also an awareness that something can be done about many conflicts from which students suffer. We as well as the students are less willing to remain idle in the face of harmful influences that could be minimized or removed. The most urgent factor in the present situation is that we can ill afford to lose capable young men and women because of their temporary inability to deal successfully with some of the problems of late adolescence and young adulthood. As my colleague,

Dean of Freshmen F. Skiddy von Stade, Jr. says, "When so many capable youngsters are on the beach it makes good sense to have expert lifeguards when some of them go beyond their depth."[1]

Since 1926, the growth of psychiatric services in colleges has been slow and gradual, but in the last decade there appears to have been a more rapid rate of increase in their numbers and an upsurge of interest in the whole problem. More than a hundred colleges had such services in 1953,[2] and it is probable, judging from the attendance and activities of the Mental Health Section of the American College Health Association, that this number is now considerably greater.

The questions most often posed to those of us working in the field is: What is the true situation regarding the incidence of various psychiatric disorders among college students? Are the constantly increasing academic requirements causing large numbers of students to "break down"? Are college students more disturbed now than formerly? Is it true that the brighter the group of students the higher the incidence of emotional disorders? What can be done to help those students whose academic careers are threatened by crippling emotional conflict, especially when little or no psychiatric help is available?

The answers to these questions, or at least opinions based on clinical experience with college students in quandaries, will form much of the content of this book.

Educators are generally united in their belief that many college students have serious and disabling emotional conflicts, that many of them can be treated successfully, and that many of them could and should be prevented. Furthermore, recent changes in the social and cultural climate favor the development of a willingness and a capacity to recognize their problems. Psychological orientation and insights are increasing, feelings of shame about mental and emotional problems decreasing. But such progress is very slow.

From the experiences of the relatively few colleges and universities which have comprehensive mental health services (usually in the larger institutions), the following estimates of the clinical problem can be made:

For every 10,000 students,

> 1000 will have emotional conflicts of sufficient severity to warrant professional help,
>
> 300 to 400 will have feelings of depression severe enough to impair their efficiency,
>
> 100 to 200 will be apathetic and unable to organize their efforts—"I can't make myself want to work,"
>
> 20 to 50 will be so adversely affected by past family experiences that they will be unable to control their impulses (character disorders),
>
> 5 to 20 will attempt suicide and 1 to 3 will succeed,
>
> 15 to 25 will become ill enough to require treatment in a mental hospital.

Of those who leave college because of mental and emotional illness, a considerable number return and are graduated (see Chapter V). Some of the most capable students are in this group. The favorable prognosis of those who receive good treatment suggests that colleges cannot ignore their problems. Some colleges (probably the majority) do little about them, because of lack of awareness of what is happening, for lack of money or professional resources, or because their administrators do not consider these problems a proper concern for educators.

Those who work in college psychiatric services do not consider it the duty of the college to furnish extensive psychiatric treatment to all students who need it: that would be too expensive even if adequate professional help were available, which it is not, except in certain large cities. They *do* think that colleges should attempt to arrange and maintain their curricula, extracurricular activities, and living conditions in such a manner so as to avoid increasing emotional handicaps of their students. All are in agreement that some effective methods of preventing failure due to emotional causes should be devised.

Everyone, in or out of college, must face stress and cope with it. The essential task of education is learning to overcome handicaps and to use one's abilities as effectively as possible. Certain background factors increase vulnerability to stress (Chapter VI). Knowledge of them can decrease their influence and help develop effective methods of dealing with life situations.

At first glance, the inclusion of a psychiatric service among those provided by a college seems superfluous. It might be said (and has been by many) that anyone who needs psychiatric treatment should not be in college. He should postpone entering, or take time out if he is already in attendance, and obtain therapy and resume his studies when his course of treatment has been completed. This point of view implies that there is a clear delineation between those who are well and those who are sick. But such is not the case. A "sick" person may be able to perform brilliantly in many of his endeavors. A "well" person may be experiencing very serious emotional distress but still be able to function in such a manner that no one could detect the strain under which he is working. The sickest person may perform well in some ways, while the normal person may exhibit some types of behavior which, if observed out of context, might be considered quite unusual.[3]

In any institution of higher learning, the sources of stress are numerous, and some people show signs of distress as a result. Occasionally, a student or faculty member becomes psychotic. Feuds originate from prolonged misunderstandings among faculty members. Interpersonal difficulties at home may interfere with the efficiency of a student or teacher, making temporary adjustments necessary if unbearable emotional strain is to be avoided. Many physicians, social workers and psychologists do an excellent job reducing such stress to bearable proportions, but the presence of a competent psychiatrist should be helpful in strengthening their efforts.

A college mental health program should be expected to alter the attitudes of many people in the institution, or in some instances to strengthen those already current. The program should encourage a greater willingness to consider the causes of behavior while attempting to improve it, and discourage the tendency to generalize without evidence, to indulge in "black and white" thinking, and to oversimplify complex issues. The basic assumptions of such a program are that behavior can be changed by slow steady pressures from respected sources, with less emphasis on force or punitive measures and more emphasis on example and group approval of mature behavior, and that discipline can be maintained by methods that are scrupulously fair to the individuals at fault if strenuous efforts are made to help them learn from the experience and to prevent their becoming hostile or alienated.

A college psychiatrist does not owe his position on the staff to his ability to diagnose and treat students in emotional conflict, though much of his work will be just that. Instead he should be considered as a teacher, a special kind to be sure, whose duty it is to aid students in the emotional aspects of maturation. Heretofore, this area of development has rarely been considered a part of higher education. With the growing realization that the feelings and attitudes of students are significant factors in their education, it becomes clear that a person with special interest in and knowledge of the emotions has an important role to play in the process of higher education. Such an individual, whether he be a psychiatrist, a clinical psychologist, or a social worker, cannot confine his efforts to working with students in conflict. Faculty members have fully as many emotional problems as do students, and usually they are complicated and of long standing. Furthermore, the specialist in the emotions should work with teachers and administrators (or anyone who has a counseling relationship with students) as they deal with students in class, extracurricular activities, or in planning their curriculum and their living conditions.

Much of the work of school and college psychiatrists consists of crisis intervention; in such situations it may not be clear who is a patient or, more frequently, there is no true patient nor can any person be assigned that role. Any time a teacher, administrator, or student is deeply troubled about the emotional reactions of someone to whom he has a responsibility, a talk with the college psychiatrist may be helpful. On this point Paulsen, the chief psychiatrist of the Stanford University Health Service, has said, "At the time of the crisis, an hour or two with an empathic faculty member, a counselor, administrator, or psychiatrist may diminish the emotional intensity of the situation to a point where it can be easily handled by the student. This is one vital form of maturation."[4] In crisis intervention, the usual rules of confidentiality apply just as they do in more formal or prolonged contacts with patients. The goal in crisis intervention is to attain a clear idea of the issues involved and some leads as to how they may be resolved. All persons involved should learn something from the experience and emerge more mature and less vulnerable. Similarly, many of the consultations with individuals center on reality problems with which a student is struggling; a traditional psychiatric diagnosis from the official nomenclature may be neither necesary nor appropriate. A "diagnosis" in the sense described by Menninger, Mayman, and Pruyser[5] is highly desirable, but at the same time attempts should be made to avoid having students who seek help for relatively transient problems type themselves as "ex-patients" because they have consulted a psychiatrist.

Warning against too early diagnosis based on inadequate assessment of evidence, the first Salmon Lecturer, Adolf Meyer, said: "There is a widespread notion among the public, and possibly also in the medical profession, that what you have to do in these disorders is to get a formal diagnosis as the result of some more or less specific and remarkable test or trick, and that this diagnosis is then used to prescribe a very particular treatment. If you mean by diagnosis a knowledge and understanding of what the moving forces are and how they *work* and how they can be modified, you are on safe ground; if, however, you think you have gained much when you have found a name for the condition, you deceive yourselves."[6]

College psychiatry is in some ways a prototype of community psychiatry. The treatment of individuals is supplemented by the use of psychiatric principles in dealing with the public health aspects of the college. It is the individual brief psychotherapy that makes the application of the public health concept possible. It is not likely that a college psychiatric program could succeed unless some provision is made for taking care of troubled people, even though this is not done in a definitive way. What the psychiatrist learns from the care of the troubled students gives him the appropriate material for helping his colleagues in the academic disciplines to work more effectively with their students. When psychiatrists work in cooperation with deans and other faculty members on behalf of students, a great many more people in the institution become skilled in identifying, understanding, and helping troubled students. If the college psychiatrist did not share his knowledge in a general way with his colleagues in other parts of the college or university, there would be no reason for his presence on the college staff. Psychiatric treatment might just as well be given by private psychiatrists who practice in the neighborhood of the college.

Within the two decades following World War II, the role of psychiatry in the United States has undergone a profound change. From a predominant emphasis on recognition and treatment of the psychopathology of the individual suffering from emotional conflict or mental illness, a shift has occurred to a consideration of the mental illness and health of all the people. This change was brought about by the efforts of many persons in psychiatry and the social sciences who believed that our knowledge of the extent of mental and emotional illness was grossly inadequate. Dr. Kenneth Appel of the University of Pennsylvania was chiefly instrumental in persuading the leaders of the American Psychiatric Association, the American Medical Association, and later on, the Congress of the United States to establish a Joint Commission on Mental Illness and Health to make a thorough study of the needs in this field. The resultant series of reports, summarized in *Action for Mental Health*,[7] has formed the basis for the development of a vast amount of planning for better mental health facilities in every state and territory of the country. This new emphasis is usually described as "community psychiatry," the basic element of which is the ideal of furnishing whatever help is available for those who are in emotional distress in their own communities and with as little dislocation of their lives as possible.

Stimuli derived from the reports of the Joint Commission on Mental Health and the subsequent legislation enacted by the Congress of the United States have initiated a great series of changes in the care of the mentally ill and in programs designed to minimize the causes of such illness at their points of origin. In colleges, the basic causes of emotional conflict or discontent are somewhat different, but still comparable to those in the general population. Not only does a college psychiatrist have the interpersonal and intrapersonal quandaries common to all young people growing up, but he must also think in terms of anti-intellectual peer group pressures, the influence of social regulations on student behavior, the anti-intellectual effects of too much emphasis on social activity, professionalized athletics, and the various aspects of the social system which bring about unrest (as discussed in Chapter VIII).

Psychiatrists in those institutions which have accepted the idea that their services go beyond that of consulting with students in conflict are often called upon to express opinions about a wide range of matters affecting practically all divisions of the college or university. The director of admissions may seek help in evaluating data concerning applicants which suggest an emotional handicap. Officials who readmit students who have left college for any reason may and should request psychiatric consultation when emotional illness has been present. The president (or his assistants) may ask advice regarding the significance of bizarre or threatening communications to his office. The librarian may request an opinion about antisocial or destructive behavior of some of those who use the library (a frequent occurrence). Individual faculty members may desire consultation about the possible significance of disorganized or pseudological term or examination papers that have been submitted to them. Student advisers may request group discussions concerning the nature of their responsibilities and ways of discharging them with greatest effectiveness. All these contacts with a wide variety of people throughout the institution serve as opportunities for furthering understanding of the nature and diversity of emotional stress and recognizing the point at which it becomes disabling.

Opinions differ as to whether student problems stem mainly from environmental factors or from disturbances in interpersonal relations in their earlier years. At the First International Conference on Student Mental Health[8] some representatives were quite convinced that the environmental factors were more important than the interpersonal ones. Most, however, put greater emphasis on earlier experiences than on conditions prevailing in college. When psychiatrists and psychologists from different countries meet to discuss the problems of student mental health in their own localities, there seems to be little difference in the type of reaction that students exhibit from one country to another.

The big difference lies in the attitudes of university officials, students, and their parents toward the nature of the psychological problems. These range all the way from denying that such problems really exist to very sophisticated psychological attitudes involving an awareness of the psychodynamics involved. To those of us with considerable experience with college students it seems clear that the great majority of psychological problems encountered by them have their origin in interpersonal relations occurring before college entrance, rather than in the new environment. Hard work resulting from attempts to meet the high standards set by a college or university is not a significant cause of emotional disorder unless there is gross disproportion between the potential intellectual capacity of students and what is expected of them.

A complex problem involved in developing college health services is the establishment of a balance between supply and demand. If the college administrators are made aware of the nature and extent of the problems among their students, and then told what can be done about them, and if they accept these formulations, the next question is, "How shall we set up a service, and where do we get the psychiatrists to run it?" This is a difficult point, because there are not enough psychiatrists to supply these demands, particularly in those colleges situated at a distance from urban training centers. Since psychiatrists who do work with college students seem to enjoy it very much, the obvious answer to this problem is to train a sufficient number of them in this area so that they may spend one to two days a week with the colleges nearest them, and do private practice the rest of the time, or work with other institutions in the community.

The solution for college mental health programs is not to have more psychiatrists and more individual psychotherapy. There are simply too many problems, too many people in trouble, and too few psychiatrists to follow this plan. Large services, such as those in a few of the big universities, are attempting to learn how to utilize psychiatrists' skills and time more efficiently than currently is done. They are not necessarily to be considered as models for other colleges to imitate. In a sense, the large services with research units constitute an attempt to learn how to get along with smaller services yet still utilize knowledge derived from observation of disturbed students in improving the education of all students.

To point up the necessity of learning to utilize all agencies in dealing with emotional problems of students it is only necessary to reflect that we have more than 50,000,000 boys and girls, young men and women, in our schools and colleges. If 10 per cent of them need professional help each year, as seems a reasonable estimate, the 5,000,000 "patients" would require the entire time of all our psychiatrists (assuming that they could all abandon or conclude their present tasks). The 16,000 psychiatrists would each have more than 300 disturbed young people under care, an adequate load indeed. Thus the answer to the problem of how best to facilitate the emotional maturation of students cannot in most instances include furnishing individual psychiatric consultations to all who might reasonably be expected to profit by them. The help of all our clinical psychologists and psychiatric social workers added to the efforts of psychiatrists would not essentially alter the fact that far more than the professional counselors must be involved. This is a task for all teachers and administrators, aided by the professional "caretakers"* in the institutions and the surrounding communities.

Erikson states that in dealing with a problem as complicated as meeting the needs of college students, theoretical coordination of the central problems should be discussed. Otherwise, as he says, general opinions and isolated practical considerations will take over. He believes that psychoanalysis and his theory of ego identity will serve as a good platform for any type of discussion, and with this I strongly agree.

A college psychiatrist who is not familiar with psychoanalysis may find himself at a considerable disadvantage in working with students. A rigid or unyielding attitude of opposition to any of the major components of modern psychiatry is out of

---

* The term "caretaking professions," introduced by Dr. Erich Lindemann, refers to all those professions that seek to help resolve personal quandaries of people—psychiatrists, other physicians, psychologists, social workers, lawyers, judges, parole officials, those who work in various family and social agencies, clergymen, teachers and all types of counselors.

place in the college setting. The publications of Erikson[9] and Sanford[10, 11] have been of particular relevance to problems of college students, but advances in psychopharmacology have been of much benefit in some instances.

Ross has cautioned against mixing therapy and education on the grounds that treatment will interfere with the educative process.[12] The teacher's primary purpose is to teach and to encourage the student to use his intellectual capacities to the greatest possible extent, whether for practical purposes or for his own enjoyment. He is the person who sets standards and tries to increase both motivation and the rewards of good work. Both teachers and parents should confine themselves for the most part to the open, above-board, obvious elements in a given situation. Psychiatry, on the other hand, is concerned to a large extent with the pathological, with unconscious motivation, with things that are not immediately apparent. Psychotherapy deals primarily with feelings and their distortions, and particularly with how they color relationships. The therapist's job is to free the energy which the student is using unprofitably in attempts to solve conflicts or to defend himself against them so that it can be used for intellectual purposes which will benefit and satisfy him.

Teachers and parents may be able to do their work better if they have some knowledge of psychodynamic psychiatry or its principles, but they should not delve into this area for treatment purposes. In short, the teacher utilizes conscious material and educational tools, while the psychotherapist deals with the unconscious as well as uses the special skills of the trained professional. Mixing the teaching of academic subjects with psychotherapy is an unfortunate practice from all points of view. The teacher is not primarily concerned with impulse expression, but the therapist may be. The therapist attempts to free the student's ego for appropriate and desired tasks. Ross agrees with Kubie that the task of the therapist is to increase the area of conscious control and decrease the more automatic, irresponsible, and rigid unconscious control.[13]

If faculty members are to do the major portion of the counseling that is done in most colleges, it is evident that some risks will have to be assumed. Inevitably, some will suffer from a confusion of roles. A few teachers will become so preoccupied with their counseling that they may neglect their classroom duties. Others will develop over-simplified schemes of counseling or evolve naive theories of personality development, furthering them with misguided enthusiasm. The harm that is likely to be done by the few who are not skillful will probably be small compared to that done by ignoring the emotional aspects of student maturation. Some of the safeguards that can be provided faculty counselors are elaborated in Chapter X.

REFERENCES

1. Personal Communication.
2. GUNDLE, S., AND KRAFT, A.: Mental health programs in American colleges and universities, *Bull. Menninger Clin., 20*:63, 1956.
3. BOND, E.: *One Mind Common to All.* New York, Macmillan, 1958, pp. 5-7.
4. PAULSEN, J. A.: College students in trouble, *Atlantic Monthly, 214*:97, 1964.
5. MENNINGER, K., MAYMAN, M., AND PRUYSER, P.: *The Vital Balance.* New York, Viking, 1963, pp. 35-48.
6. LIEF, A.: *The Commonsense Psychiatry of Adolf Meyer.* New York, McGraw-Hill, 1948, pp. 497-498.
7. ——————: *Action for Mental Health.* New York, Basic Books, 1961.
8. FUNKENSTEIN, D. H., Ed.: *The Student and Mental Health—An International View.* New York, World Federation for Mental Health, 1959, pp. 16-17 and 271-275.
9. ERIKSON, E. H.: The problem of ego identity. *J. Psychoanal.,* 1956.
10. SANFORD, N., Ed.: *The American College.* New York, Wiley, 1962.
11. ——————, Ed.: *College and Character.* New York, Wiley, 1964.
12. ROSS, H.: In: *The Student and Mental Health—An International View.* Funkenstein, D. H., Ed. New York, World Federation for Mental Health, 1959, pp. 127-142.
13. KUBIE, L. S.: *Neurotic Distortion of the Creative Process.* Lawrence, Univ. Kansas Press, 1961, pp. 137-143.

CHAPTER II

ADMINISTRATIVE ASPECTS OF COLLEGE PSYCHIATRY

COLLEGE PRESIDENTS AND trustees are faced with constantly increasing demands for new services and facilities for their students. The numbers of students in most colleges are also becoming greater year by year, and much care must be exercised to see that any new programs undertaken will be justified and more desirable than those plans which must be rejected. This chapter is devoted to a consideration of the factors which are relevant to decisions about the establishment of programs to aid in the emotional maturation of students and guidelines for their operation.

Every college has many persons in it who devote a considerable portion of their energies to aiding the emotional maturation of students. All too often, however, there is a lack of coordination among the officials or faculty members who have such responsibilities. Without adequate coordination of counseling, troubled students may not be directed to the source of help best suited to their needs. Since the way students feel about their college experience is a very important factor in their motivation, it is desirable that someone always be available to discuss their reactions with them. When possible there should be specialists in emotional development, and particularly in emotional conflict, available for consultation by those teachers who counsel students, especially when severe psychic problems are suspected.

In a formal program, the psychiatrist is a key person, at least in theory. He is the professional whose main task is the study and treatment of abnormal behavior. A complete college per-

sonnel program includes individuals who are concerned with
finances, religion, discipline, public relations, behavior in the
classrooms and dormitories, deficiencies in the vocabulary of
learning and in relations between faculty members and students,
and among students. The central official in the coordination of
personnel services is usually the dean of students.

The health program is somewhat difficult to fit into the other
personnel services. If it is to be maximally effective, it should
have the best physicians available, and, of course, the demands
for their services are great. As I have stated elsewhere, I believe
that the health service should be an independent agency working
closely with the dean of students and his colleagues, but reporting
to the president's office.[1]

Under this type of organization, the psychiatrist should be
attached to the college health service but he should have good
relations with all other persons who are in direct contact with
students. The less the amount of psychiatric time available, the
more it should be devoted to consulting with teachers, deans,
heads of departments, and other counselors, based on the sup-
position that a thorough understanding of abnormal behavior
will be of some help in preventing it. Because psychiatrists are
in short supply, numerous health services in major universities in
the United States have social workers and psychologists who work
as a team with the psychiatrist in dealing with the many emotional
conflicts which students need help in resolving.

The work of members of a college psychiatric service is varied
and may at times involve contact or cooperation with any member
of the institution. Possible activities include caring for disturbed
students (or others as appropriate), arranging for referrals, consulting in crisis situations with students, parents, teachers,
administrators, community officials, or other counselors, teaching
(usually as guest lecturers in various courses in which emotional
factors are being considered), and participating in research on
late adolescent and early adult development. Staff members
should keep themselves informed of potentially explosive situations throughout the institution. Many problems of which out-
siders are seldom aware are of great concern to anyone attempting
to maintain an environment conducive to learning. Library

vandalism, cheating and plagiarism, stealing in the college and community stores or in the dormitories, unacceptable or antisocial sexual practices (overt homosexuality, exhibitionism, promiscuity), and the unwise and unregulated use of harmful drugs are examples of behavior that suggest the presence of emotionally unstable persons and which call for administrative action when the participants are known.

The identification of those who offend the community cannot be done by the college psychiatrist from the information which patients give him in confidence. The psychiatrist may (and should) strive to help the patient indulging in such behavior become sufficiently responsible to refrain from it. He should also let the patient know that if he is caught he must suffer the consequences. Furthermore, it is entirely ethical for him to work with all other responsible persons in the college to minimize antisocial behavior, so long as he does not violate the confidence of patients. This should be made quite clear to students and faculty alike. Those who insist that psychiatrists and other counselors must report unacceptable behavior to disciplinary authorities may not realize that students who seek help for their quandaries, of which the need for control of antisocial behavior is one, are already attempting to acquire self-discipline. To undercut them by unethical behavior would not only cause others to avoid the counseling sources but deprive them of valuable help in resolving their difficulties (see Chapter XI).

Almost every college has a problem with students who act out their difficulties at the expense of the local stores. Occasionally a disturbed student who is not in financial distress will steal books or other articles more as an expression of his emotional disturbance than as an indication of need. Regardless of the psychological motives for such stealing, the student must be held responsible for his acts, and must be dealt with in an effective manner. Those who steal from sheer perversity should be handled in one manner. Those who do so because of overwhelming emotional impulses should be referred for medical treatment. The indications are not always clear as to which causes are preponderant. In any case, the offending student must be studied sufficiently so that rehabilitative measures undertaken are appropriate and effective.

One of the areas in which students and others most actively work out their psychological problems is the library. Practically any college librarian could produce a tale of woe that would shock those who are not familiar with his problems. Stealing books is an ever-present problem, and seems to be growing in frequency. Mutilating books by cutting out certain sections desired by the reader, cutting out material which is offensive to a particular disturbed patient, and defacing books by obscenities are common practices. Occasional persons suffering from sexual abnormalities resort to libraries for their voyeuristic or other pathological activities. Whatever the senseless acts of vandalism may be, there is no question but that those who commit them are often seriously disturbed persons.

Department heads, deans, and presidents are frequently the recipients of threatening communications from persons who think themselves harmed in one way or another by these officials. A proper task of the college psychiatrist is to keep informed about these individuals, discuss their activities with appropriate persons —members of their families, the police, hospital officials, or the individuals themselves. Since the people who commit these acts are usually disturbed, it is quite essential that they be handled with respect for their disabilities and that punitive attitudes be kept to a minimum. Sometimes, of course, as with anonymous threatening telephone calls, the whole apparatus of law enforcement must be brought into play in order to find the individual whose actions are unacceptable.

The question may well be raised, "Is the psychiatrist an arm of the administration or not?" The answer to this is difficult because in some ways he is and in other ways he is not. In general, it is the duty of the psychiatrist to look at the various situations that arise from the point of view of the individual who is most disturbed and who is presumably causing the difficulty. Certainly, the psychiatrist is not retained by the college to be an administrator or a policeman. Neither should he be required to betray any confidences. His job is to help individuals who suffer from emotional conflict in whatever way he can. He should be an interpreter of the nature of such behavior and should know how it can be kept under reasonable control with justice to the individual who happens to be its victim.

A college psychiatrist (or any physician in the health service) should not have the power to make administrative decisions for the college other than those that are strictly medical in character. Among the latter are decisions regarding entrance to or discharge from the infirmary or a hospital or permission to leave the infirmary to attend classes. Disciplinary problems arising in an infirmary should be handled by the physician until or unless the unacceptable behavior calls for a serious penalty; at that point the authority of the dean should be sought.

College officials occasionally use the psychiatrist as the authority for a decision that may be disagreeable to the persons affected; this impairs the future usefulness of the psychiatrist and in the long run weakens the authority of the dean or president. The psychiatrist should have the privilege of being heard when appropriate, and his recommendations should be seriously considered, but only the duly constituted college authority has access to all the information that is available for an equitable decision. It follows logically that a college psychiatrist should not expect all his recommendations to be carried out; if none of them are heeded he might well examine his own status in the community. In short, he is a friend of the emotionally disturbed or mentally ill, even when he may have to become involved in actions which, for the moment, are unacceptable to them. His task is to improve the level of mental health of everyone connected with the institution. If the senior members of the administration of a college do not have confidence in the judgment of the psychiatrist, it is better to have none than to have someone who cannot be trusted.

Psychiatrists are in great demand everywhere. In general, a psychiatrist who is engaged full-time will have to be paid at the level of the senior professors, and if this scale is not sufficient to attract a desirable psychiatrist, he can be given permission to have enough private practice to make up the difference, at least in part, between what the college can afford to pay him and what he could otherwise earn. However theoretically desirable it might be for a college psychiatrist's practice to be restricted to students, there are many situations in which it is highly desirable that he see persons connected with the institution on a private basis. A psychiatrist may, therefore, be serving the institution best when he devotes the main part of his efforts to the students but is also allowed, through flexible regulations, to contribute to the mental health needs of the entire community. A good psychiatric service is expensive. It is only a question of whether it may not be even more expensive not to have one.

To answer the often-asked question, "What is the appropriate size and cost of a 'reasonable' mental health service for a given institution?" Wilms, the Director of the Psychiatric Division of the Purdue University Health Service, made a survey of seven leading universities known to have mental health activities of moderate scope within their student health centers.[2] Those universities with unusually large psychiatric services were not queried, nor were those with associated medical schools.

In this group 2.3 to 6.2 patients per 100 population were seen each year, the average being 4.4. Each person was seen, on the average, five times each year, ordinarily for the customary fifty minutes. Group sessions were not counted.

A full-time clinician (psychiatrist, psychologist, psychiatric social worker, trainee) was defined as one who works forty hours a week. Adding those who are on a part-time basis, and making the necessary calculations, it was learned that the universities ranged from 0.19 to 0.42 full-time professional workers per 1000 students, the average being .32. Each full-time person or the equivalent averaged 654 interviews yearly, with a range of 440 to 854.

The average yearly cost was $3.27 per student enrolled, with a range of $2.09 to $4.60.

Compared to the costs at Harvard University these are quite modest. In the same year (1963-64), 1,205 of Harvard's 13,871 students were seen an average of five times each. There were 8.25 full-time clinicians based on a forty-hour week, the number per 1,000 students was 1.68 and each psychiatrist had an average of 730 interviews. The cost for each student was $9.17 (based on salaries alone).

Wilms analyzes the various factors that influence costs, requests for services, and how practices vary in understaffed services as compared to those with more adequate staff. It is a reasonable assumption that whatever professional time is available will be completely occupied by students requesting help. No college or university has yet succeeded in meeting all requests for psychiatric help, and it is not clear that this should be attempted. The essential point to be made from these crude statistics is that even a meager mental health service will cost $3.00 per student enrolled in the college and a reasonably adequate one will cost two to four times that much, depending upon many variables, only a few of which have thus far been mentioned.

The most common of the objections to the establishment or elaboration of a mental health service is that it is not needed. On one occasion on which I was outlining the need for competent attention to the emotional maturation of college students to a group of distinguished citizens, one of them said, "When I was at Blank College in 1923, everything was all right—what is the problem now?" Such a person deserves an answer, but an attempt to give it is somewhat like persuading a fish that he should stay in water. The frames of reference of a college psychiatrist and an old grad who has a romantic memory of his carefree college days are so different that communication is unusually difficult.

Some people believe that emotional problems will only increase in severity if attention is paid to them; at times they may also express the fear that contact with a psychiatrist will cause an illness that would not otherwise have occurred. For proof they point out that a certain person of their acquaintance was getting along well and working effectively until he consulted a psychiatrist, following which he became quite disturbed and had to go to a mental hospital for a while.

Others, particularly in the medical profession, are uneasy about the current emphasis on the emotional aspects of illness and imply that specialization is being overdone. A director of a college health service who deplores this tendency said, "Mental health is an area about which so much is being said these days on all levels of society. My feeling is that too much publicity is being given to the need for specialized help. I would be the first to say that certainly we need psychiatric help for some of our students, but I abhor the thought that everyone should be screened, treated, or consulted by (sic) a psychiatrist, psychologist, or social worker when most needs can be cared for by the patiently listening G. P. or a faculty or religious counselor and plain old fashioned common sense."[3]

Although practically all faculty members favor professional attention to acutely disturbed students, there are some who resent being involved in any way in cooperative efforts between psychiatrists or other counselors and teachers in solving students' quandaries. This attitude was clearly evident in the reply of a professor in a large state university to a request from a college psychiatrist for help: "I am paid to teach, not to be a nursemaid to weaklings!"—following which he slammed the telephone receiver down, dramatically ending the conversation.

A more subtle form of opposition, and one with much support, concerns the tendency to increase the responsibilities of faculty members to the point of impairing their effectiveness. "Teachers cannot be at once teachers, psychiatrists, medical men, and social reformers; they waste precious time whenever they fret themselves and their charges over questions that are social in origin and that no teacher and no school can solve singlehanded."[4]

Another critic warns against the use of psychiatry in our schools, saying that psychiatry is an "institutionalized purveyor of moral values" and that "those most eager to get religion out of the public school are the most eager to get psychiatry into it." He also states that "the more attention the school pays to 'mental health' the less it pays to education; hence, education is bound to suffer." He refers to psychiatric practices as "the application, to so-called mentally ill persons, of systems of poorly articulated ethics." After a long series of warnings against the use of "psychiatric influences" in our schools he adds as an additional bit of generosity, "The advocates of some of the most evil schemes of human depredation—especially in this, the twentieth century—have claimed to be animated by motives of helpfulness."[5]

A college president or dean is often approached by a parent who objects to the type of treatment being given his son or daughter or even to the fact that contacts with a psychiatrist, psychologist, or social worker were permitted at all. For example, one woman whose son was particularly resentful of what he saw as her attempts to continue domination of him far beyond the time he considered appropriate had pressed him to tell her what he and the psychiatrist discussed. When he told her she became quite angry, later complaining to the president that she knew her son had no such thoughts and that the psychiatrist must be putting those ideas into her son's mind.

The parent who threatens a lawsuit against the college because his offspring was permitted to see a psychiatrist has no grounds for it if the psychiatrist has conducted himself in a manner consistent with professional ethics and the usual customs of the health service. The legal counsel for the college or university should be kept informed of all such threats or complaints; he can then be helpful in keeping the anxiety of the psychiatrist, president, or dean under control. If an error has been made it should be admitted at once, the reasons for it made clear, and appropriate apologies made. Nothing encourages a contentious person so much as being received by college officials with an attitude similar to his own. The proverb "A soft answer turneth away wrath" is still good psychology.

Some administrators fear that if a psychiatric division of their health service becomes well and favorably known their admissions offices will be besieged by students who have psychiatric problems and see the possibility of getting "free" treatment after admission. This problem has not yet become noticeable on a significant scale, and as the number of colleges with competent psychiatric services increases the possibility that it will develop lessens. Perhaps it is not a legitimate concern in any case, since there is no evidence that young adults in college who are known to need help in their emotional development are any less capable in later life than those who are not in distress during their college years. The conspicuous "troublemakers" are not numerous enough to offset this generalization.

Another objection, quite the opposite of the one just outlined, is that no students who need help are enrolled in the college, and that if they were, these students would not want or use the service. This objection is heard only when those who voice it are not aware of the opinions and feelings of the students. The experience of the University of Toronto is representative of many institutions whose psychiatric and other counseling services are not yet fully developed.

Student government officials there, in an effort to find out whether the students needed and wanted counseling, sent a questionnaire to a random sample of 500 students to which they received 400 replies (80 per cent of the group). In answer to appropriate questions, it was learned that 50 per cent of the men and 64 per cent of the women expressed a desire for counseling. Emotional problems ranked first among their concerns, followed by financial, social, academic, religious, ethical and medical problems. Seventy-two per cent of the men and 74 per cent of the women said that they had suffered from some despondency or depression during the preceding year. Types of problems included lack of self-confidence, poor adjustment or unsatisfactory relations with the opposite sex, too much to study, confusion about values, and frustrations with conditions at home. More than a third of the students said that they were close to a nervous breakdown. Seventeen per cent of the men and 30 per cent of the women said that they had contemplated suicide. Tranquilizers were said to have been used sometime during the year by 37 per cent of the men and 36 per cent of the women.

Regardless of the technical accuracy of this questionnaire survey, the overwhelming impression is that the students were troubled and that they did want help.[6]

Since the competence of a college psychiatrist is the most important factor in the success or failure of a program, desirable qualities should be considered prior to selection. To be sure, many colleges have no choice other than to engage some of the time of whatever psychiatrist may be available or do without one entirely; if the psychiatrist who is available does not measure up to reasonable expectations, it is better not to become involved with him. The most important issue is the competence of the individual who heads the mental health program, not the type of training to which he has been exposed.

First of all, a psychiatrist contemplating entering college psychiatry as a career should secure a well-rounded training in general psychiatry, with considerable emphasis being given to growth and development and the emotional disorders of childhood. His intellectual interests should be broad and his curiosity boundless, for he will be working with young people who are eager and questioning, engaged in an unending variety of undertakings, and who in many instances will have more potential intellectual capacity than he himself possesses. He should be able to communicate with his professional colleagues in the technical manner appropriate to his discipline, but in conversing with his academic colleagues or with students he should be able to express the most complex psychological concepts in simple and understandable terms.

In a college community, he will be well-known if successful; he should therefore be able to tolerate many associations with his patients outside his office, seeming to ignore the private relationship without being ostentatiously careful about doing so. Since he has personal knowledge about individuals which he has acquired in strict privacy, he must be very discreet and avoid inadvertant disclosures. He should be able to present ideas to groups in a clear and concise manner; since preventive psychiatry is a prime reason for his presence on the campus, he should utilize every available channel for improving conditions favorable to the development of responsibility, integrity, and satisfying modes of living. It is not necessary that he belong to any particular "school" of psychiatry. In fact, he should preferably have a broad view and acquaintance with all forms of theory and treatment but without strong antipathies to any one; obviously he will have preferences, but he need not be fanatic in agreement or disagreement with a particular set of theories. In practice, it is very important that he have a keen awareness of the multiplicity of influences that may give rise to emotional conflict. These may stem from genetic, biochemical, environmental, familial, social, cultural, racial, or religious sources—all concepts that may overlap with any of the others but which must be understood in terms of the individual student's immediate situation. This comprehensive emphasis on the totality of experiences and biological qualities of which an individual consists is called psychodynamics. Stated somewhat more formally, psychodynamics includes the whole body of knowledge about biological and social forces which influence personal behavior in psychological ways. In practice, attention is usually focused on certain intermediary psychological processes, such as interpersonal attitudes, repressed desires, and emotional conflicts.[7]

REFERENCES

1. FARNSWORTH, D. L., Ed.: *College Health Administration.* New York, Appleton, 1964, p. 9.
2. WILMS, J. H.: How much for mental health? *J. Amer. Coll. Health Ass., 13*:422-430, 1965.
3. LONGEST, J. C.: The college student health service: a general practice institution, *J. Mississippi Med. Ass., v*:229-233, 1964.
4. BARZUN, J.: *Of Human Freedom.* Rev. Ed. Philadelphia and New York, Lippincott, 1964, p. 149.
5. SZASZ, T.: Psychiatry in public schools. *Teachers Coll. Rec., 66*:63, 1964.
6. Personal Communication: Mr. Paul Becker, World University Service of Canada.
7. WHITEHORN, J. C., Ed.: *Psychiatry and Medical Education.* Washington, Amer. Psychiatric Ass., 1952, p. 100.

CHAPTER III

DEVELOPMENTAL TASKS OF
COLLEGE STUDENTS

Of all the theories of personality development Erik Erikson has formulated the one which is most useful to those who would understand the late adolescent and early adult. He postulates that from birth onward a child is continually confronted with a series of decisions, crises, or problems whose nature he must comprehend and for which appropriate adaptations must be made if his further development is to be as favorable as possible. He divides the various stages of development into eight groups: infancy, early childhood, the play age, school age, adolescence, young adulthood, adulthood, and old age. If the tasks of each period are accomplished successfully those of the next age are more likely to be mastered than if the problems of a given period are not solved. These separate stages are of course divided arbitrarily, but they do conform with reasonable faithfulness to the life tasks which are characteristic of our society and culture. The stages leading up to young adulthood will be reviewed briefly.*

In the *first period,* which includes the first fifteen months of life, the child acquires either a general sense of optimism or pessimism toward other human beings and particularly his father and mother. He acquires a preponderance of feelings of trust or an attitude of basic mistrust. If he is fed when he is hungry, dried when he is wet, cleaned when he is dirty, and loved when

---

* The most comprehensive statement of Erikson's views in this area may be found in *Childhood and Society,* 2nd Edition, New York, W. W. Norton & Co., 1964, p. 247-274.

he is lonely, he gradually acquires confidence in others and the feeling that human beings are friendly and that he can take chances. He learns that he can be alone for a while and that those who love him will come back to him. If, on the other hand, his needs are carelessly or thoughtlessly met, or if he is neglected, a general mistrust develops which impairs his later personality development. It is not the quantity of love that is so important at this period as the quality of the relationship—particularly that with his mother. It is significant to recall at this point that practically all young people who are at serious odds with their environment have had a very difficult home life in their early years. Basic trust and basic mistrust are the great alternatives in this period.

The *second stage,* that of *early childhood,* is the one in which the child has the task of learning how to regulate his behavior in such a way as to keep the affection and esteem of his parents and at the same time to gain control of himself and to develop confidence in his own ability to progress still further. This is the period when bowel and bladder training are central issues; they must be handled carefully if they are not to give rise to later emotional conflict. If outer control is too rigid, the child may not develop appropriately. If, on the other hand, there is no pressure towards self-control, he may continue in his inappropriate behavior. A successful outcome of this period is a sense of control without loss of self-esteem. If the main tasks of this period are not accomplished successfully, a lasting sense of doubt and shame results. Autonomy or shame and doubt are the two extremes that may result.

In the next period, the *play age,* the child explores his environment to see what he can and should do and what he can become, and what are the limits to his activity. He learns from those about him what is expected of him, what kind of initiative he can profitably and safely express to meet his wants. He begins to see goals beyond those connected with his immediate family. Slowly he puts together all those admonitions and prohibitions which he has learned from those who are important to him and organizes them into a system of principles which begin to guide his behavior. This is the beginning of conscience. During this period his resentments toward those who stand in the way of his wishes may be quite intense. He may wish to get rid of them and this brings about feelings of guilt. He struggles with those feelings and with a sense of inferiority. If he finds that he can make a place for himself without wishing harm to those who are close to him, particularly members of his family, his confidence increases and guilt feelings decrease. If his sense of guilt is increased by methods of child rearing which continually emphasize shame and faultfinding, he may develop an overly-strong conscience, one which functions in a very automatic and rigid manner and impairs his judgment later on. Initiative or guilt are the two polar outcomes.

The next phase, the *school age,* is one of slow steady development. He learns to win recognition by producing things. He develops good work habits. He tends to idealize the parent of the opposite sex and identify with the parent of the same sex. Close friendships are formed with members of his own sex but considerable disdain is exhibited for members of the opposite sex. By gaining recognition and esteem for things he does well, he learns that work can be enjoyable. If he is always criticized for what he does poorly he may never achieve enjoyment of his work. If he does not receive appropriate recognition for what he does well, he may develop a permanent sense of inadequacy and inferiority. Industry or inferiority are the alternatives.

In the *fifth stage,* the period of adolescence, the major task is the *achievement of identity;* if success is not attained, role confusion or even a negative identity ensues. The adolescent, like the younger child, has certain basic emotional needs which should be met if he is to make a satisfactory record in school and in the community. He needs affection from family and friends, the feeling of belonging and being needed, and he appreciates being treated as a separate person rather than as an extension of his parents. A favorable climate for growth and the development of security calls for freedom from excessive domination or interference in his affairs, but just as surely it includes firm discipline from persons he respects. Change should not be too rapid or frequent and provision should be made for alternation of stimulation and relaxation together with some privacy. Experience should have meaning for him and usually this suggests that he should have a sense of accomplishment and status in his community. Encouragement by giving credit for tasks well done is more apt to influence motivation favorably than is severe criticism for poor accomplishment. When learning has personal meaning and is related to an individual's interests, goals, and values, there is seldom any problem of motivation. The satisfaction of these basic needs is originally the responsibility of the family, aided later by churches, schools, and society in general.

Some, and perhaps the majority, of adolescents react in a healthy way if their earlier tasks have been mastered successfully, if their defenses are good, and if they have love, acceptance, and respect. They can then sublimate their new energy. Others may be overwhelmed, react with severe anxiety, and become withdrawn, rigid, inhibited, constricted, and ineffective. Another group may act out their feelings. Usually, if the earlier relationships are not good and moral standards are low, they give in to their impulses.

During adolescence itself, phantasy life is increased, and narcissism becomes prominent; there may be some near megalomania as an attempt to still anxiety. There is marked ambivalence, i.e., a desire to be like adults and a need to be like children. All the glamour of growing up is bombarded by the security of being a child in the family.

Adolescents often accuse their parents of being old-fashioned, stuffy and prudish, out of touch, too rigid, and not treating their friends as they themselves expect youngsters to treat their own friends. Some youngsters say that the parents seem bored with them and that this makes them feel separated; others say that parents don't do enough with the children. Some of them say they want their parents' cultural and intellectual standards to be raised; others complain because their parents cannot control their own emotions and because they displace their irritations onto the youngsters.

Parents, on the other hand, sometimes complain because the youngsters do not seem to have initiative, because they get angry with their parents so easily, because they think the world will give them want they want, because the children would rather be more like each other than follow their own individual preferences. They feel that they cannot talk with their young teenage children; they feel lost in their relations with them because the youngsters never seem interested in their parents' problems. Many parents are worried about having their children "go steady," and about their manners.

The adolescent fights hard against attempts to correct him. He fights doubly hard when he is wrong, especially if he knows it. He is frequently in a reverse phase. He is often guided by his peers, his gang, others who feel as he does, a leader with whom he can identify. This helps him to break away from his parents, gives him a sense of power, a feeling that he can do things, a feeling of belonging again. Many of them can act aggressively without breaking over into delinquency. Bravado, shamelessness, contempt of parents are all encouraged by the group. The guilt is absorbed by the group. This is very difficult for the parents to tolerate. Defiance is bad enough, but contempt is worse. Such attitudes must be recognized as a temporary defense to help the adolescent break away from his parents with a minimum of suffering. The love for the parents is still there, but there is a lessening of dependency in it. The love relationship with the parents should not break off completely.

Adolescents frequently say to their parents, "You just don't understand. You are old. You are a fossil. Kids are different." In effect they are saying, "The more decent you are to me, the sooner I can come back to you." It takes much stability, strength, and courage to accept this behavior and remain firm. Parents must take the attitude that they are going to stand by. They should accept the attacks and the fighting back without becoming extremely anxious about it. Such adolescent behavior is not pathological. Toleration is possible only if parents really love the child and remember their own stormy adolescence. "I'll watch and wait and see what happens." These situations call for caution rather than quick action. Information should be acquired and the hostility accepted. Eventually, the child is freed from conflict so that he can go on and do his work. In neurotic and delinquent children, the period before adolescence is frequently filled with stress.

The adolescent who spends much effort and energy in "acting out" his troubles is not unusual. "Acting out" is aggressive anti-social behavior which expresses underlying conflict. It is quite different from psychoneurosis. Most of these youngsters are in a chronic state of tension and unrest. They are basically unhappy and insecure. Many of them feel rejected and live on the pleasure principle, being unwilling and unable to accept frustration. They see little to gain by conforming to what society expects of them. They frequently feel like punishing their parents. They fail to develop the necessary social controls. Such factors as poor nutrition, inadequate rest or sleep, over-stimulation, and illness frequently decrease the young person's ability to tolerate frustration. Many of these rebellious adolescents resent their status in life. They hate the restrictions imposed by society and give vent to their feelings by vandalism and sadistic attacks on animals or persons. They seem to make a vain effort to lessen their accumulated guilt and tension. They may tease or annoy other youngsters, usually those younger than themselves. Such individuals frequently feel the need for authority, preferably exerted by a person they can love or respect. A good relationship has to be established before authority has much effect on them.

Stealing is frequently, but not necessarily, a neurotic form of behavior. The child may get advantage from what he steals. Quite often, however, stealing is a kind of symbolic behavior in which the young person is trying to get something which will replace the love which he feels he has not obtained. It also has an element of revenge. When the parent of an adolescent destroys the young person's confidence in him, for example, if the father deserts the mother, or if the mother becomes disloyal or alcoholic, the young person then may feel free to abandon the standards which the parents have previously taught him.

Sometimes young persons who have run afoul of the law may run away from institutions a few hours or days before they are scheduled to be legally released by the authorities. When this occurs they have, in effect, attained enough comfort to get along in the institution, but they cannot trust themselves to tolerate freedom on the outside. Adolescents desire independence, but they are also often threatened by it.

The problems of adolescence usually cannot be treated by the development of deep insights. Sometimes the youngsters are angered by attempts to get at the deeper reasons for their behavior. There is little to be gained by such attempts. Instead, work should be done on the present situation, on the ego strength. Controls should be exerted, preferably in the form of firm discipline from a respected source. These individuals need limits and want them. Behind their mad drive for control is the desire to be helped. As soon as the parent loses authority, the youngster is ripe for delinquency. Mature feelings of sex come late in adolescence, and sexual activity should be delayed. The delinquent, however, is most likely to "act out" sexual relations quite early.

If the problems of adolescence are met successfully, the individual is in a far better position to achieve the capacity for intimacy, creativeness, and responsibility for others, and integrity, than if his solutions to problems of this period have been faulty.

If the disturbances of adolescence are to be understood, one must look to the quality of his current experiences and factors in his developmental experiences. The nature of the relations with members of his own family is very important. As the adolescent approaches maturity, new forms of behavior must be developed which are not inherent in any of his earlier experience. As he approaches adulthood, forms of anxiety which are reminiscent of those in his earlier experience may become prominent and disabling. The adolescent must be able to see the reasons for the position taken by his parents so that he can relate them to what he sees elsewhere. Such an understanding enables him to separate himself in his thinking from his parents and to develop new goals and ideas.

What the adolescent thinks of himself, and what he thinks others think of him, are the chief ingredients from which his sense of identity develops. When these two are in reasonable harmony and are satisfying to him he develops a new perspective on his family and on society and can view himself in this framework.

Each new maturational step involves relinquishment of older forms of behavior and relationships by the young person and his parents. Sometimes the relationships between the child and his parents are such that this upward-moving development is very difficult. One or the other or all concerned try to keep the others in a dependent position.

It seems reasonable that the adolescent is much affected by what he sees as parental expectations. When these are inconsistent, the tendency will be for the young person to have a diffusion of identity.

When parents are themselves needful and immature, they tend to develop dependency upon their adolescent children. Such parents are often threatened by their children's developing abilities, and tend to deprecate and minimize them in various ways. Parents may become very dependent upon their children as they mature but, when the children express needs of their own, become resentful and antagonistic.

When students arrive at college they have much unfinished business insofar as attaining maturity is concerned. Yet this is the period which society more or less arbitrarily assumes as marking the beginning of adulthood. College administrators and teachers make the same assumption, or they should make it, yet with reservations based on the knowledge that no one can make the transition from childhood to adulthood without firm support, for a while, from those who love and respect him most. The following tasks are of central importance.*

1. Changing from relations of dependence upon one's parents and other older people to those of independence

This process should have begun early in life; it reaches its culmination during the college years. Constructive rebellion may signify success, apathy and resignation reveal failure. Rebellion which is uncritical, unfocussed, and indefinitely continued usually suggests the tragedy of long-continued psychological deficiencies in earlier stages of development.

Parents often appear in a much less favorable light to college students who are struggling to become independent than they

* These are modified somewhat from those first published in Report No. 32 of the Group for the Advancement of Psychiatry.

did earlier or will later in life. Their strong effect on their children is an accurate index of their importance. No influence is more important in the character development of children than that exerted by parents. Nearly all parents try very hard to do what is best for their children. In late adolescence and young adulthood, children may be very harsh in their judgments of their parents. The following observations concerning parents portray them, not necessarily as they are, but as they appear to their children who are in the later stages of adolescence and in early adulthood.

Among the most common influences in the background of college students which contribute to inhibiting or incapacitating conflicts in them are conflicts between their parents. Practically all couples have disagreements from time to time. Those that are open and resolved in a reasonable manner, even with outspoken arguments or quarrels, probably harm the children little; they may even help them learn how to handle their differences with their fellows. Those which are hidden, subtle, or involve inconsistent and neurotic behavior patterns are likely to be devastating. Broken families do not of themselves produce mentally disturbed youngsters. It is a question of what kinds of emotional strains have upset the family structure and how the children have reacted to those strains. Conditions which appear quite similar to the casual observer may be inhibiting and destructive to one child yet stimulating and constructive to another. When one parent attempts to win the support and loyalty of the children against the other, the children are put in an intolerable position; they cannot show open affection for one parent without risking the loss of the affection of the other. Consequently, a cautious withdrawal from open emotional expression may result, leaving a somewhat constricted personality.

Some parents are unable by reason of their own personal problems to engage in a healthy expression of their feelings even when it is appropriate to do so. This inhibits the development of the children's capacity for honest expression of feelings. Others over-protect their children, which discourages the necessary experimentation required for mastery of their environment. The desirable degree of freedom for appropriate development of self-control and independence involves risks to children and requires courage on the part of parents.

Many parents are so busy trying to maintain a high material standard of living for their families that they have too little time to invest in close companionship with their children, particularly in the adolescent period. The youngsters themselves may also develop habits that take them away from home influences. The result may be that there is little opportunity for identification with the parents; the children may not have adequate ideas of the nature and scope of feminine and masculine roles. It is a short step from this to the children's conclusion that their parents do not really care, absorbed as they seem to be in their own affairs.

Some children encounter strong criticism from their parents and teachers for every shortcoming or mistake, with little commendation for the things in which they do well. They grow up full of doubts about their own ability. Their sense of competence and self-reliance does not develop. They expect failure and are constantly preparing for it. Thus their energies are diverted from accomplishing their aims to devising defenses against unfulfilled expectations.

Without realizing it, some parents, in their zeal to give their children the greatest possible support, seem to look upon them merely as extensions of themselves, rather than as separate persons in their own right. The children soon come to believe that their parents' interest in their accomplishments stems from anticipated reflected credit and is greater than their sincere desire to see their children do well for their own sake. Children often sense this difference quite early in adolescence and feel uncomfortable about it. "You can't do that—what will the neighbors think?" expresses the priority involved.

Many college students are pursuing their studies for excellent reasons—but not their own. A father may be eager for a medical career for his son; he may push hard to interest him in this endeavor, or he may use the soft-sell method and try to hide every evidence of such a desire. But his attitude is obvious. As one young man said, "I went to medical school for my father, now I'm going to law school for myself." A mother may have been unhappy about her own school experience and do everything in her power to see that her daughter does something different. Occasionally the college student may truly want to pursue a certain course of study or career, but because his parents have so strongly urged it he rebels by partial or complete failure until he can be helped to sort out the conflicting motivations. As one student whose parents had exerted pressure for him to study engineering said, "The hell of it is I really want to go into engineering."

Some college students are handicapped by having come from homes in which books, magazines, and interesting conversation were missing and by the fact that their parents were not interested in learning. Consequently they were unable to encourage their children's interest in academic subjects. Often young people who grow up in such homes never reach college, but constitute a group from which we could recruit more able young men and women and help overcome our deficit in skilled manpower.

2. Dealing with authority

The handling of authority poses a special problem for many college students. Still in the process of achieving independence from their parents and in forming an identity of their own, they are in rebellion against many of the customs or opinions about which they had had strong feelings earlier in life. Displacement of negative feelings from their parents to the college or to some of its officials is quite common. Their attitudes toward the college's use of authority remains ambivalent; although they expect limits to be set on their behavior, they resent their enforcement. If discipline is lacking, or authority is exercised inconsistently or with favoritism, resentment is intense.

Rule believes that it makes little difference whether parents are restrictive or permissive, order or persuade, run a "loose" or a "tight" ship. It is *why* they act as they do that matters. If parental actions are truly in the interest of the child and are basically selfless, the child will sense this and his personality development will reflect it.[1]

During the college years, young men and women probably have more freedom of behavior than they ever had before or ever will have again. They have discarded many of the constrictions imposed by their families of origin and have usually not assumed the responsibilities of new families. The tendency is strong to throw off the restraints to which they have been accustomed and to experiment with new forms of behavior. They often appear to want all the advantages of independence without giving up any of the advantages of being dependent upon their parents. They may seem to lack consideration for the rights and comfort of others. In their zeal to get rid of the old and embrace the new, they criticize the values of their parents mercilessly. They may refuse to write to them for weeks or months at a time. They may adopt unusual mannerisms and styles of clothing that they know will displease their elders. Personal cleanliness and other sanitary habits may border on the primitive, particularly if they have been taught high standards of personal care. It is only logical that, when students undergo such drastic changes in their behavior within weeks or months of matriculation, parents should blame the colleges for the apparent deterioration. Yet, neither the admonitions of the parents nor stern warnings from proctors, deans, or house mothers produce prompt or lasting improvement in behavior. Parents often must be told as delicately as possible that college officials cannot change such behavior in thousands of students when they (the parents) are unable to do it even for one person.

When college officials do not interfere with students who are trying to work out their emotional conflicts in these dramatic and mildly antisocial ways, it may seem to indicate that the officials are either uninterested in or unable to maintain discipline. Yet, no college approves behavior which is destructive to the reputation of the students indulging in it or to that of the college itself. What college officials strive for is an environment in which students may learn how to acquire mature habits of thought and behavior, develop potential creativity, and learn to be independent without being unnecessarily offensive to those who may not agree with them. The limits are clearly defined, but they are applied with restraint and thoughtfulness, not with impulsive anger. To apply sanctions in a punitive manner at this period of development only perpetuates the undesirable behavior and makes the rebellion more intense, more painful, and more prolonged. Punitive action seems to justify the young person's resentment and to postpone or prevent the acquisition of self-control. A college should be a place in which students try out new ideas and forms of behavior, but which provides safeguards to keep them from destroying their careers in the process, and also from making public nuisances of themselves.

3. Learning to deal with uncertainty and ambiguity, particularly in matters involving the balance between love and hatred

The art of disagreeing vigorously with others without hating them is an important aspect of maturity. In a democracy, this is an essential ingredient. In international relations, it is even more important, and failure to live up to this ideal will bring about the ultimate tragedy if the disagreeing nations happen to be those with a wellstocked nuclear arsenal.

In political life, opponents often speak as if they had only contempt for one another, wheras in reality they may get along well personally. Their followers, however, may not be aware of the "rules of the game" and as a result engage in actions very destructive to society.

Many young persons do not realize that love and hate are closely intertwined. They may feel that their sentiments should be of the all-or-none variety. This results in rigidity and intolerance, making them prime propects for hate groups that thrive on persons who are fearful, hostile, and prejudiced.

One painful form that uncertainty may take may be called the dilemma of choice. When students came from rural and restricted environments, the choice of course or career was usually not a complicated process. There were relatively few possibilities. One did as the society directed, though choice was possible within narrow limits. These choices could be made with a considerable feeling of freedom. Acceptance of whatever fate appeared to have in store was easy because there was nothing much else that one could do.

Now all this is largely changed. Opportunities, good or bad, are almost limitless. Instead of certainty, students face uncertainty. They have incurred the dilemma of choice. As an old Dutch proverb clearly expresses the situation, "He who has a choice has a problem."

Making a choice would be simple were it not for the consequences. Let us consider the kind of life one wishes to live. For girls, will it be marriage or a career? Or is such a choice necessary? Many young women think marriage is compatible with a career, though the latter would be pursued less intensively or even temporarily set aside during the child-bearing period. Others do not see how marriage can be combined with outside activities. This leaves unanswered the question of what those women between the ages of forty and seventy are to do who have not prepared themselves for some kind of productive activity, whether for pleasure or profit or both.

If one wishes to teach, then what? Teaching involves teaching a subject. Each discipline is becoming increasingly complex year by year. Preparation to the level of high competence takes more and more time. If one begins with one area of concentration, or major subject, and thereafter loses interest, much more time is lost in selecting a new subject than when things were simpler. Making a choice, moreover, rules out many other possibilities, any one of which might have been as interesting and rewarding as the one chosen. This may make one feel trapped— the very opposite of freedom.

The same principle holds in making most of our other truly important choices. Though anything may be possible, everything is not possible.

In many other areas, students must learn to deal with ambiguity and uncertainty. Attendance at college has been said by one observer to be society's most elaborate device for the artificial postponement of adulthood that could be imagined.[2] This delay is related to the principle that organisms that have a long period of relative immaturity or development are far more advanced than those which mature in a comparatively short time. One might say that a premature assumption of adult tasks before one's intellectual capacities have been realized may prevent such a realization. But for the student the quandary becomes, "How can I remain effective, feel a sense of meaning and purpose, and yet not know precisely what I am preparing myself to do?"

4. Developing a mature sexuality

No more complex problem now confronts educational

administrators in this country than that of fostering conditions in our colleges that permit the development of wholesome attitudes about sex, marriage, and the family. Such attitudes are necessary to the development of people of character and integrity.

In recent years, sex has been emphasized in all aspects of society to a degree that has become alarming, distasteful, or boring, depending upon one's point of view. Advertisers, novelists, playwrights, and fashion designers have all exploited sex with seeming disregard of the dangers inherent in such a course, in many instances reassuring themselves and others in pious word and manner that what they are doing is truly moral and uplifting. Thousands of stimuli now impinge upon the consciousness of young people, encouraging them to abandon old standards and to exercise complete freedom.

The older generation has little to say of a constructive nature on sexual standards of behavior aside from those upheld by religion. The confusion is so great that most people have lost sight of the fact that a sexual morality of some kind is necessary even in the most primitive societies as well as for those who profess no religion. Instead of helping young people develop responsible attitudes and behavior in this field, we have, as a people, added confusion rather than clarity to their thinking.

I do not believe that our present late adolescents and early adults are in the mood to do what they are told in this or any other controversial field of behavior. But they should be granted the privilege of objective dialogues on the subject with older persons who perhaps know the consequences of behavior. If they are to come up with proper answers, they must first have a sound understanding of the nature of the issues involved. The colleges are not engaged in a conspiracy to keep knowledge away from their students. They simply do not know how to proceed in an area so filled with uncertainty and dangers. (For a fuller discussion of this problem see Chapter IX.)

5. Finding security, developing feelings of adequacy or competence, and attaining prestige or esteem

The family originally furnished, or should ideally have furnished, these stabilizing components. During the college years each person must internalize this process and maintain his own standards and emotional climate.

Children need the feeling of belonging to a certain region or community. Many are never able to experience this emotion because their parents, whether because of military service or frequent transfers by the companies for which they work, move the family frequently during the school years. Some of these children grow up "rootless," with few ties to any locality and few close friends. Even more regrettable is their inability to form close associations even though quite intelligent; they have no real feeling of selfhood; they feel empty.

The highly capable boy or girl who attends a school in which his capacities are never seriously challenged may become so accustomed to dependence upon his ingenuity, rather than on systematic application to his studies, that he never develops good study habits or experiences the enjoyment of intellectual pursuits. When such a person is admitted to a college where students are highly selected and capable he may not be able to develop the necessary perseverance to compete successfully with his more disciplined colleagues, even though his intellectual endowment is as great as theirs.

Recent research confirms a principle that has been accepted intuitively or as a result of experience, namely, that academic progress is more rapid when a student is stimulated to work to capacity and when there are frequent changes of conditions under which he works to permit and encourage the development of versatility.[3] Just how intense the stimuli and how frequent the changes should be has not been ascertained, and probably varies from one person to another. But psychiatrists and others who work with college students believe the excessive contrasts between the prevailing values in the home and community from which a student comes and those upheld in the college he enters may be a source of emotional distress, often sufficient to cause the student to withdraw from college. A student whose home background includes fundamentalism in religion, rigid customs regarding relations between different races, "black and white" attitudes and opinions about politics, and little encouragement to engage in intellectual activities but strong emphasis on material advancement may find the opinions and attitudes which he observes in his college associates very disturbing.

There are obviously many other influences impinging upon every child which may in extreme situations give rise to crippling indecision but which usually provide practice in resolving conflicts. The quality of his teachers, peer-group pressures, characteristics of the neighborhood in which he lives, nature of his religious training—all these and many others affect every child. Occasionally a particular combination of undesirable influences brings about tragedy for a child while other children, apparently in the same circumstances, develop normally. Every child's thoughts and feelings are peculiar to himself and may be distressing in a seemingly favorable environment or quite satisfying in an apparently detrimental one.

When a student goes to college, stress and conflict are inevitable, even necessary, for rapid progress toward maturity. For many, it is their first extended period away from home. They meet many other students whose ideas and ideals differ widely from theirs. Higher standards of academic performances are expected, different both in quantity and quality from those which seemed to get them through high or preparatory school. They may sense strong pressures to make a choice of career early or to choose between marriage and a career. College is the place to test the ideas they have acquired and to try new ones. Never again will they have such freedom to examine, to test, to discard what is unsatisfactory and to adopt a way of life which promises to be rewarding.

Because of the enormous influence on contemporary thought of the work of Erik Erikson, the concept of identity and its corresponding negative and role-diffusing phases are so well-known that nearly every college student with personal conflict assumes that he is suffering from an "identity crisis," whether in fact he is or not. I even knew of one college sophomore who announced in a large discussion group that she was then in the third month of her identity crisis. Many students read into Erikson, as they do into Freud, interpretations never envisaged by the authors.

Observations of students whose transition from adolescence

to adulthood has been relatively painless (and these have generally felt a warmer support from their parents than those who
experience crises) suggests that a feeling that the past and the
future are related is most important in enabling such transitions
to be made smoothly. Here again, Erikson's comments are
perceptive: "Like a trapeze artist the young person in the middle
of vigorous motion must let go of his safe hold of childhood and
reach out for a firm grasp on adulthood, depending for a breath-
less interval on a relatedness between the past and the future,
and on the reliability of those he must let go of, and those who
will receive him." But this capacity does not come easily or
automatically. "The young person, in order to experience whole-
ness, must feel a progressive continuity between that which he has
come to be during the long years of childhood and that which
he conceives himself to be and that which he sees others to see
in him and to expect of him."[4]

6. Development of standards and value systems

If the original admirable desires of the students, the goals of
the curriculum planners, and the highest ideals of education as
expressed in philosophical terms could somehow be coordinated
and implemented, the college experience might be far more
influential than it now is. Unfortunately, many peer-group
pressures, influences of the mass media of communication, and
attitudes displayed by persons outside the colleges show the
balance of values, tastes, and standards to be toward mediocrity
or worse. Individual students should be aided in developing high
ideals in the face of overwhelming pressures toward low ones.

In a society in which an individual who strives for high
standards of taste and conduct has difficulty in making his
influence felt, while the person who seeks to debase and destroy
these standards can readily achieve wide influence, it is of the
utmost importance that many people become concerned about
how values are developed and how they are transmitted from
the older to younger generations. The simplest way to discover
how this transmission takes place is to ask oneself, "How did I
get the ideals, standards, and values which I prize most highly?
From my parents? From my friends or teachers? From religion?

Or from a combination of these and many other sources?"

Most students will find that they have acquired their ideas of what is desirable from many sources, but that the main influences have come from those closest to them and whom they love (or want to love), their parents. Each person creates his own particular combination of values; through thought and effort he can improve them. If the initial inculcation of values has been positive rather than negative, constructive rather than destructive, good rather than bad, the individual soon develops his own built-in corrective devices enabling him to check his errors and learn from them. The person who has been so unfortunate as to have had a preponderance of poor examples set for him in his formative years naturally has a much more difficult task in acquiring self-direction and all too often becomes a periodic victim of his own impulsive, unwise actions, because he has not developed the capacity to learn from experience.

In the past, we have often assumed that if only we could make education available to everyone who could take advantage of it most of our problems would disappear. It was vainly hoped that knowledge would automatically bring responsibility with it. We have now become thoroughly disillusioned on this point as a result of the catastrophic events initiated repeatedly in this century by countries with a highly educated citizenry. We have learned that knowledge without virtue is dangerous. Sanford has said: "Intellect without humane feeling can be monstrous, whereas feeling without intelligence is childish."[5] But we have not yet learned how best to develop character, nor are our institutions of higher learning sufficiently concerned about their responsibility or aware that the task in large part belongs to them.

While helping college students master the tasks described above it is often essential that administrators and teachers acquire knowledge about students of great delicacy and complexity. Dr. Benson Snyder, Chief Psychiatrist of the Massachusetts Institute of Technology's Medical Department, asks the question, "What information does the college professor or administrator need to have in order to understand the educational impact of his school on the educability of his students?" and points out that students (as well as faculty members) keep private many of their disappointments regarding the college experience. Exposure of such feelings may be painful or even dangerous. Prying into such secrets may be resented, and applying pressure for disclosure unethical; privacy must be respected. In trying to understand what is going on in a student or group of students, it is helpful to know what may be considered safe to talk about and what may be risky or dangerous. Knowledge of students' private opinions is not easy to acquire but is necessary to understand how they integrate the college experience into their lives and relate it to past experience and future expectations. Such knowledge is vital to understanding an educational institution in depth. It is in the acquisition of knowledge-in-depth of a college that all types of counselors can be helpful, but associated problems of confidentiality must be thoroughly understood.[6]

A major problem faced by an increasing number of our young people is the discrepancy between the enormous number of stimuli to which they are subjected and the small amount of satisfaction they receive from each stimulus or from the total impression made by all the stimuli. As parents and teachers, we are emphasizing quantity at the expense of quality. Students feel that they must work hard to get into the right schools or colleges rather than because of the inherent satisfactions of mastering a subject. A thirteen-year-old pupil said of her school work recently, "When you get interested in something and they (the teachers) force you to do too much work in it, you lose your interest." She was referring to a crucial point in the learning process—interest increases motivation, some kinds of pressure stifle it. A young student certainly cannot be left entirely to his own devices; similarly he should not have native interest killed by well-meant but excessive pressures.

The essential element in encouraging motivation in young people lies in the models for emulation provided by parents and teachers. The students will tend to imitate what they see practiced by their elders whom they respect rather than what they are told they should do. The sad truth is that the task of the colleges is constantly being undermined by those whose interests are temporarily better served by low rather than high tastes and standards of behavior.

In the next few years, we will probably see more and more friction between students and administration in American colleges. A variety of factors suggests such a development. Faculty members seem to students to place a higher value on their research and work with graduate students than on teaching undergraduates. The recent publications entitled *The Flight From Teaching*[7] and *Is There a Teacher on the Faculty?*[8] highlight this problem. Whether as a result of this or not, contact between faculty members and students is frequently sparse or unrewarding to both. Many students are pushing for their "rights," often encouraged by organizations that have long been active in defending the rights of minority groups who have been exploited. It is understandable that, as students feel the increasing impersonality of higher education, they should protest, even if they often do not use good judgment about when to protest, what to oppose, or even in the choice of targets for their hostility.*

I see no way to avoid such crises in student-administration relations if faculty members maintain a "hands off" or "it's none of my affair" attitude. Relations between students and teachers are the heart of the educational process. Teachers should be as much concerned about the people they teach as the subjects they teach. Concern with the emotional development of college students should no longer be considered out of bounds by those who plan the programs of institutions of higher learning.

REFERENCES

1. RULE, J. T.: The parental dilemma, *Pediatrics, 35*:494, 1965.
2. ERIKSON, E. H.: In: *Student and Mental Health: An International View.* Funkenstein, D. H., Ed. New York, World Federation for Mental Health, 1959, p. 74.
3. SANFORD, N.: Factors related to the effectiveness of student interaction with the college social system. In: B. Barger and E. E. Hall, Eds.: *Higher Education and Mental Health.* (Proceedings of a Conference, 1963), Univ. of Florida, p. 13.

---

* See Chapter VIII for a fuller discussion of this issue.

4. ERIKSON, E. H.: *Insight and Responsibility*. New York, Norton, 1964, pp. 90-91.
5. SANFORD, N.: *College and Character*. New York, Wiley, 1964. p. 284.
6. SNYDER, B. R.: Personality needs and personality factors in undergraduate education. Proceedings of the Symposium on Undergraduate Environment, Oct. 18-19, 1962, Bowdoin College, 1963, pp. 22-27.
7. —————: *The Flight From Teaching*. New York, Carnegie Found. (reprinted from the 1963-64 Annual Report).
8. FISCHER, J.: The editor's easy chair: Is there a teacher on the faculty? *Harper's Magazine, 230*:14-28, 1965.

CHAPTER IV

CLINICAL PROBLEMS

T HOSE STUDENTS WHO experience unusual difficulty in completing the tasks of early adulthood may show it in various ways. Without knowledge of a student's thoughts and feelings about himself and others, his choice of symptom or behavior to express his distress appears to have no logical basis. With such knowledge his symptoms and his behavior usually become comprehensible and as a result more amenable to management or change. Only the student can describe his own emotional reactions; when he trusts his counselor or therapist he can do this much more easily than when he feels he will not be understood. It should be emphasized that insight into his own feelings and attitudes does not automatically produce a change in a student's behavior. If insight alone could correct emotional distress and inappropriate actions, there would be little need for psychotherapy; education alone would solve all our emotional problems.

Psychotherapy, when successful, involves a gradual development of new habit patterns that are satisfying and constructive to replace the older inhibiting and destructive ones. It is in this area of removing impediments to learning that the goals of liberal education and educational psychiatry coincide. The aim of both is to free the individual so that he can explore ideas of which he would not otherwise be aware—education, by introducing them to the student, and educational psychiatry, by minimizing or removing the psychological conflicts that would otherwise deflect his energies from constructive channels.

Students who are having difficulty in assuming the responsibilities of adulthood usually manage to overcome their handicaps through their own efforts, aided frequently by their friends, counselors, or parents. Those who have some capacity to appreciate others' views of them have a greater capacity for such favorable development than those who are largely self-centered.

Some students are impelled to oppose everything that has wide acceptance or approval. They are in revolt against respectability and convention in all forms. Whether the target be cleanliness, religion, fidelity, or self-control, they gain temporary satisfactions by showing their contempt. Since many of them come from families that are proud of their reputations, their choice of protest behavior often appears to have been adopted in order to bring the most painful embarrassment and humiliation to their parents. Such a course usually leads to one of the most restrictive of all forms of conformity, even though a consistently negative one. These forms of behavior do not constitute mental illness, even though students exhibiting them have their share of emotional conflicts just as do those students with highly conventional forms of outer adaptation to the forces affecting them.

The most dramatic of the problems encountered by college psychiatrists, or by college physicians or deans when no psychiatrist is available, is that of the psychotic student. No reliable data exist as to incidence of psychoses among college students, but estimates made by those who are familiar with the problem indicate that for every 1000 students about two to three will develop such an illness each year. If the estimates of those psychiatrists who work in the institutions with adequate health services hold true for all colleges, the number of students so affected among the 5,400,000 enrolled in the United States (in 1955-66) will be in the range of 11,000 to 16,000. What happens to such a large number of students is of much significance, particularly because they are potentially great assets to society, either positively in terms of what they might accomplish if treated successfully or negatively in terms of their own unhappiness and their drain on society if they have to spend their lives in mental hospitals. (See Chapter XII for a proposal for their treatment.)

In view of the complexity of the decisions that must be made about psychotic students, it is surprising that so little is known about their course, prognosis, and their chances of continuing their professional activities if they recover. A few studies have been made, small in scope to be sure, which suggest that a modest optimism in this regard is warranted.

In 1958, Harrison[1] reported a study made on 179 Yale students who had left college in the 1947-52 period. Fifty-two were diagnosed as psychotic; of these, 52 per cent returned to Yale, and of this number 78 per cent remained to graduate. Three of them (6 per cent) committed suicide. No data is available concerning the other 48 per cent who did not return, presumably some of them may have gone to other colleges. Those who were psychotic were as likely to return to Yale as those who suffered from neuroses or character disorder.

Carmen[2] made a study of thirty-five Harvard undergraduates who became psychotic, had to leave college from 1955 to 1959, and later returned. Of this group, six were hospitalized in their freshman year, nine in their sophomore year, fourteen in their junior year, and six in their senior year. Initial periods of hospitalization varied from one month to a year. About one-half had only one period in the hospital, the others two to four periods. Two-thirds were schizophrenic, the remainder depressed.

Twenty-one students (60 per cent) were graduated, seven with honors. Six were graduated with their own class, eight were graduated one year behind their class, three graduated two years behind, and four from three to five years after members of their own class had been graduated. Of the graduated students, thirteen had had acute onsets of their illness, while eight had gradual onsets. The students with gradual onsets had more prolonged and more repeated hospital stays than did those with acute onsets.

Of the fourteen who did not graduate, all but one had gradual onsets of their illness. Ten of them had more than one hospital stay. Unsuccessful attempts to complete college were made by ten of them. Three were too ill to be considered for readmission and two committed suicide.

There is a growing tendency for the larger university health centers to treat students with acute psychoses in their own infirmaries or hospitals, where staff members are prepared for such care, facilities are adequate, and the patients are not too grossly disturbed. This is a policy that should be initiated only after careful preparation and indoctrination of all personnel who will be involved. Two key factors are the skill of the nurses in the understanding and care of such patients and the maintenance of continuous communication between the nurses and the physicians in charge.

Psychiatrists from the health service of the University of California at Berkeley have reported their experiences in treating students who were sufficiently emotionally disturbed to require hospitalization during the academic year 1960-61. The student enrollment was 27,963 and 1,609 (5.75 per cent) had received some psychiatric treatment. Of this latter number, 132 (.47 per cent) were hospitalized, ninety-six in the student health facility (Cowell Memorial Hospital). Nonpsychotic emotional disturbances accounted for fifty of these, twenty-seven were acute psychotic reactions, and nineteen were chronic psychoses.

Of the twenty-seven who were acutely psychotic, ten were able to remain in school, while seventeen had to withdraw on medical leaves of absence. Of those with chronic psychoses, eight were able to stay in school and twelve had to leave. Of the fifty students with nonpsychotic severe illnesses, thirty-four were able to remain in college; sixteen had to take a leave of absence. Summing up the results of the ninety-six who were treated in the college hospital fifty-two (54.2 per cent) were able to remain in college and forty-four (45.8 per cent) took a medical leave. Of the seventeen who were acutely psychotic, three were transferred to mental hospitals for further treatment and fourteen required no further hospitalization elsewhere. The duration of hospitalization was one to thirty days, with a fairly even distribution throughout this whole range.

The authors were convinced that prompt intensive treatment of incipient or acute psychoses in young people in familiar and benign surroundings can accomplish far more in a few days or weeks than similar efforts exerted after a psychotic process has become firmly established. Furthermore, the general disruption of the students' lives—personally, academically, and socially—is greatly diminished. Many students were saved an extended period of residence in a state mental hospital; those who could have afforded private care avoided the expense of a private hospital.³

Walters has recently described a constellation of symptoms which is very common among male college students and to which he refers as *apathy*.⁴ It is expected that every student during the course of his college career will feel apathetic when the pressures of work and of his own expectations become too great. There are some students, however, who respond to a transitory stress with prolonged apathy. Such students have a total disinclination to study. They appear to the college officials and to the pyschiatrist as indifferent, languid, indolent, lethargic, dull, or apathetic. As one student expressed his plight, "I can't make myself want to study." Such students suffer reduced emotional stability, preoccupation with current work difficulties to the exclusion of past experiences and future expectations, and inability to study in spite of constant efforts. Such students describe themselves as without feelings other than those of emptiness, physical lethargy, and intellectual impotence. In some colleges the syndrome is known as the "sophomore slump," even though it may occur at all college grade levels.

Such students, by reason of disturbances in previous interpersonal relations, frequently are compelled to present themselves as weak and inadequate. Their general concepts of competition are unrealistic—they are convinced that they would readily succeed if only they exerted enough effort. In the case histories studied, in all of which there had been actual injury and/or failure of a successful parent, success and competition represented potential personal disaster similar to that experienced by the parent. Therefore it became necessary to avoid success; unused potential provided a rationalization for the student's failure.

Apathy is a defense which protects the patient or those close to him from being hurt. By living out his fantasies of being deficient, the patient prevents himself from dealing with the effects of his own aggressiveness. His strong feelings of hostility and rage toward certain people are partly diverted into anger toward other persons and partly inward onto himself, producing guilt and "failure." By turning some of his strong feelings outward, seeming to promise success, and then turning near-success into failure, the student torments and tantalizes those who helped him until they, too, are reduced to a feeling of helplessness as great as that exhibited by the patient.

Apathy may be a precursor of depression or it may be followed by neurotic symptoms. These patients have never allowed themselves to formulate clear goals and are committed to nothing. In a sense, apathy is a continuation and exaggeration of the defenses and solutions commonly used by the adolescent. Such patients have a prolonged adolescence because of unresolved conflicts centering around the formation of a masculine identity.

These students often need the opportunity to explore their own capabilities under less pressing circumstances than those presented by the college. It is in such situations that temporary interruptions in school work (a "moratorium," as Erikson has described it) are necessary. These students become "dropouts," but their temporary leaves of absence often help them to "find themselves," and they usually do quite well thereafter. Thus, a leave of absence may in effect turn out to be a continuance of education rather than an interruption. Education involves the task of mastering content, but also that of developing a knowledge of self that permits its utilization, its appropriate application. One must know what one can do and what one can't.

The following case history illustrates many of the main features of this syndrome.

Bob, a twenty-year-old junior, majoring in economics, was referred to the psychiatric service for evaluation by his senior tutor, whom he consulted because of an inability to work which had been bothering him for about three to four months. The patient had originally consulted the senior tutor about the advisability of dropping out of school; he felt that he wasn't doing any work and had no right to waste his professors' time and his parents' money. When the senior tutor first saw him, he was impressed by his earnestness and bewilderment. He referred him to special tutors for intensive work in the courses with which he was having trouble. The tutors, too, found Bob earnest and bewildered by his difficulty, but in spite of their best efforts his confusion continued and the comment most often heard was, "I don't know what is the matter with me, but I can't seem to want to study." Finally, as a last resort, Bob was referred to the psychiatric service for evaluation and treatment.

Bob repeated the same complaint to the psychiatrist, namely, that in spite of his best efforts he could not seem to study. The key word was "seem," for as Bob told the story he never really tried hard to study—the longer he sat at his desk the more his anxiety grew. The more anxious he became, the more often he either indulged in vague daydreaming of a Walter Mitty type or would join any friend who happened to come by to do anything that was not related to studying or other organized activity. As he told his story, it became plain to the psychiatrist that the apathy included not only attitudes concerning his studies but also those toward his social life and his friends. Bob shunned a great many of his old friends, who were hard-working students (as he had been); he felt himself ill-at-ease and somewhat inept with young women. He spent a great deal of time sitting around thinking about doing something. Thinking had taken the place of action for him, and he was not aware of any distinction between the two.

As the patient recalled it, this state had been slowly developing for a number of years. He was an exceptionally good student in high school, particularly during the first three years when he was very active in a high school political group and had risen to some prominence in it. He also did quite well academically and managed to do reasonably well in high school athletics. He was one of the better liked students in the high school and the one predicted as "most likely to succeed." However, in his senior year in high school he began to lose interest in his work and began to question the use of working hard. These thoughts were of great concern to him and he tried to banish them from his mind, but to no avail; they recurred even more insistently.

Bob is the second of three children, born to a very successful lawyer and his wife, who lived in a medium-sized Eastern city. His father was a college graduate, had attended a well-known law school. After a few years of floundering about, he achieved great prominence in his community, both in legal and political circles. His mother is a very competent woman, warm, housewifely, very much involved in community activities and never too busy to spend time with her children. His older sibling, a sister, three years older than he, was also very talented and attended a quite demanding college from which she had graduated with honors, and was now continuing excellent work in graduate school. He also has a brother, fours years his junior, who is beginning high school. This brother is well-liked and active, although not as talented academically as either Bob or his sister.

Bob's childhood was uneventful. He was remembered as a very sweet little child, who spent a great deal of time by himself playing with much inventive fantasy. Because of his sweetness, docility, and winsomeness he was the favorite of the family, and received a great deal of attention, particularly from his mother, who used to take him many places with her when he was quite young. As he entered school, however, he became more independent, much more active, and shied away from the maternal contract that he had previously enjoyed.

The only difficulty in this family was the poor relationship between sister and brother. The sister was a very active, aggressive girl who liked to get her own way and who would try to obtain it by physical means if she could not do it in other ways. The patient was discouraged from physical retaliation. It was not considered permissable in this family for young men to hit young ladies. There were some bad feelings between father and son on this account, since the boy at times felt that he was treated unfairly.

The patient's passage into adolescence was uneventful. He continued working quite hard. His father rose to greater prominence but was stricken, when the patient was approximately fourteen, by a severe respiratory disease which required his drastically limiting his activity and at one time resulted in an illness which came near being fatal. Following this, the father seemed to be quite depressed. The family was quite solicitous of his health and a great deal of care had to be taken around the home not to upset the father. The boy felt that this was unfair, that he couldn't fight with the father, that he couldn't rebel, that it might damage the father. He also began to wonder soon after this if it was worth working hard to achieve prominence if an act of fate struck you down at a later time. It was as if he began to wonder whether or not masculine aggressiveness was worth it all, and at this time a reversal from active to passive attitudes took place.

Because Bob's apathy involved his whole life and prevented him from taking any kind of positive action, it was necessary for him to withdraw from school. It was recommended that he seek therapy for which he would partially pay with money earned at a job he would obtain.

It is important in the handling of apathetic students to insist that they carry out some form of positive action, although it should be less complicated than school work. Most apathetic students feel sufficiently guilty because of their poor performance that they quite readily agree to get a job if encouraged to do so. Success in a job aids greatly in rebuilding their self-esteem.

Because of the provocative nature of apathy, the therapist is tempted to encourage, cajole, or even insist on the patient's return to college. Initiative that does not come from the patient is usually ineffective; if the therapist does urge the patient to action before he is ready for it, he will be identified in the patient's mind as just another person who "doesn't understand." An attitude of restrained encouragement is usually helpful, one which consistently reminds the patient of the question, "By doing nothing, what are you trying to avoid doing?"

This question will have to be asked many times before the answer, in all its myriad forms, will be understandable to the patient.

A far greater number of students who are inhibited by emotional conflict show their lack of effectiveness through changes in behavior than by developing symptoms of illness. A few indulge in serious antisocial acts, destructive to society or to themselves, behavior that seems certain to result in failure while at the same time giving them an acceptable excuse for it. Stealing, cheating, and plagiarism can often be interpreted as calls for help, but it should be made explicit that a psychological cause for such actions does not in any way lessen the responsibility of the student for his behavior. The probable causes of antisocial behavior are utilized in determining the best methods of correction, rather than in excusing the offender for any responsibility for his acts.

Although the conflicts of college students differ in no essential way from those of other young people, they are usually more easily formulated and treated for at least two reasons: (1) college students are usually able to accept and think in terms of psychological concepts and (2) they are close enough in time to the contributing factors and astute enough about their nature to be able to respond to psychotherapeutic measures rather quickly. Their defenses have not yet hardened or crystallized into fixed but inappropriate patterns. Brief psychotherapy based on psychodynamic formulation of the issues confronting individuals may have its greatest usefulness among college students.

We will now consider a few case histories designed to convey the nature of the problems with which students often have serious difficulty. These are a representative and not a comprehensive selection, since this is not a textbook of clinical psychiatry. Although all the incidents portrayed have actually occurred, all the identifying data have been altered to protect the privacy of individual students. Almost any patient could find something of himself portrayed in one of the case histories.

These cases have been selected from thousands who have sought help. They illustrate the principle that no two students' problems are the same. Each case is unique, just as each individual is unique. Running throughout all cases are numerous similarities, however. Family, and especially parental, relationships are crucial in most cases. Sexual development is a frequent source of acute concern. Each individual was seriously troubled, yet by outer, superficial standards he might not be thought of as being sick. In fact, it is hoped that students with serious and complex problems which have been solved with psychiatric help, but without the development of disabling symptoms requiring hospitalization, will not type themselves as "ex-patients." Making a diagnosis of illness (in the form of a one-word summary) before the situation is thoroughly comprehended adds nothing to understanding and may serve to discourage a dynamic evaluation of the numerous factors which unite to constitute the disability.

The relationship with the therapist is itself a part of the

therapy, even before the deeper factors are explored. The patient tries to explain his feelings and attitudes to someone who understands them and who refrains from making interpretations on partial data, or too soon, or inappropriately, thus inhibiting further examination of the issues by the patient.

The first case represents a common problem among boys—the fear of homosexuality. All persons are partly homosexual and partly heterosexual. Usually the heterosexual pattern becomes dominant during adolescence if sexual education has been adequate and the introduction to heterosexual attitudes and practices has not been unduly traumatic. Failure to achieve mature heterosexuality may be viewed as inadequate development of one aspect of personality, and therefore as susceptible to treatment as any other developmental lag. As in other areas of personality development, the earlier the treatment the more effective it is likely to be.

James, a twenty-one-year-old senior, was referred for psychiatric consultation by a faculty member (a friend of the student) to whom he had gone a few days previously in acute distress. He feared that he was homosexual because he had rather suddenly developed sexual thoughts about boys in his presence. He also feared that he would be ostracized if these thoughts became known. He sometimes thought he might act on his thoughts and make advances to boys but never did, nor did he experience any real sexual excitement, only vague, affectionate thoughts. He tried to avoid these thoughts, but the more he tried the more obsessed he became. He was preoccupied with doubts of his own masculinity. He became anxious, study and concentration were impaired, his appetite decreased, and he had trouble falling asleep. His grades took a sharp dip. Finally he decided to seek help.

At the first interview he was very carefully groomed, his manner open and hearty, and his presentation of his problem clear-cut and direct. He was obviously anxious but handled his anxiety by intellectualization and numerous obsessional defenses. His therapist felt as if he were talking about a third person as he described his own symptoms. Beneath the surface of a well-dressed, well-mannered young man there was obviously an anxious and frightened little boy. When his parents were told by their son of his troubles they offered to help him, even to the point of paying for prolonged psychotherapy if needed.

His disturbing thoughts had arisen after a series of discouraging episodes sparked by taking a course which was too difficult for him because he lacked the important prerequisites for it. He worked harder and harder, became increasingly discouraged, and finally found difficulty even with courses ordinarily easy for him.

Coincident with his academic problems came dissatisfaction with girl friends. The girl whose company he most enjoyed was not intellectually stimulating. Their relationship was becoming more intense in the sexual area than he desired. When he began dating other girls, they seemed to show little interest in him. Another blow came when he failed to make a varsity team.

Disturbing dreams evoked his fears of homosexuality. A typical one involved going into a room which looked like his room at home. A beautiful girl lay in his bed. He became sexually excited but when he started to make love to her she turned into a boy whom he did not recognize. He awoke agitated and confused.

Later on in therapy he recalled that while on a trip with a group of people an older man of whom he was fond made homosexual advances to him in a hotel room. He resisted the advances but only vaguely remembered what happened. He had also once engaged in mutual masturbation at age fourteen with a boy his own age.

Gradually, he and his therapist explored his relations with his parents, an older brother, and his female friends. There was no particularly outstanding deficiency in these, though it was noteworthy that his father had suggested that he provide himself with contraceptives when he went to college, but at the same time warned him not to get into trouble. Being gradually reassured that he was not a homosexual, his work with his therapist enabled him to develop more realistic knowledge about heterosexuality.

After a few weekly interviews, his depressed feelings began to lift. A connection between the intensity of his unacceptable feelings and the degree of difficulty of his studies soon became evident; as his problems increased, his self-confidence was impaired. He soon became aware of long-standing conflicts between himself and his father over issues of dependence and competence. He and his very successful father had been in considerable conflict over a career choice for the patient. He developed the ability to talk with his father about these differences and found that some of his opinions as to what his father thought were quite unjustified. His feelings about other members of his family became clearer to him. The periods of preoccupation with homosexual fears decreased in number and duration, tending to recur when he was in competition with men.

His dating practices gradually became consistent with common heterosexual patterns, and his relations with his roommates became more mature in character. His grades were improved—in fact, they were higher than before his illness. Therapy was discontinued not long after his homosexual thoughts disappeared. Several months later he reported no recurrence. According to the patient, his major accomplishment in therapy was that he had become more observant and perceptive about his own feelings and those of other people.

The next case of a young woman illustrates how complex the problem of fear of homosexuality is, and also demonstrates the traumatic effects of unfortunate exposure to homosexual behavior, all the more serious because it involved a close relative. Some psychiatrists might believe that the patient should have prolonged and intensive therapy, that brief treatment would be of little help and that she would become ill later on. Our experience suggests that brief psychotherapy is helpful, that its effects often are lasting, and that if further treatment is needed later on the patients are more accepting of it than if they have not had previous help.

Margery, a tall, slender nineteen-year-old girl in her third year of college came to the clinic self-referred, stating, "I don't know if I can get this all out, but I think I am a homosexual." Her feelings, because of their complexity, were difficult for her to articulate. When finally she was able to verbalize them, she became aware that her expressed fear of being homosexual (an unusual presenting symptom among the women students) was but one facet of a deep-seated depression having as its core the death of her father several years before. This depression was precipitated by the recent termination of a close relationship with an older man.

For the past year and a half, Margery had been plagued by feelings of "loneliness, isolation, worthlessness, inadequacy, a self-destructive tendency, and an ever peristent fear of being a homosexual." At times she was unable to study or engage in any meaningful activity. Her symptoms were experienced for the first time soon after her return to college, following a "wonderful summer." She spent this summer working among Negro teen-agers in a large Midwestern city. There she met an older man, a married Negro social worker, with whom she formed her first close relationship. Her return to college in the fall abruptly terminated this relationship and marked the onset of her symptoms.

Margery was puzzled by her preoccupation with homosexuality. She had had no homosexual experience. Nevertheless she was haunted by a gnawing fear that she was destined to become homosexual. This issue pervaded the first few sessions. She asked many questions about latent homosexuality. She thought that she was frigid and had read that frigidity was caused by latent homosexuality. She thought that this intense concern might be related to an experience she had had two years previously when she found a member of her family having homosexual relations with a neighbor.

This occurred when she was seventeen years old and inadvertently walked into her mother's bedroom to find her mother having sexual relations with another woman, a neighbor and friend of the family for many years. This neighbor, like her her mother, was widowed. The patient was shaken by this experience. Afterwards, she had occasional doubts about her sexual identity, but these doubts did not preoccupy her until the occurrence of her symptoms two years later.

The support and reassurance that often suffices to resolve the doubts concerning one's femininity or masculinity common among people of this age proved to no avail. Each attempt to reassure the patient that there was little evidence to indicate that she was homosexual and that her feelings were part of the normal processes of maturing was parried by the patient's accusing the therapist of attempting to manipulate her thoughts. "I think you know that I have a real homosexual problem, but you won't tell me. Instead, you merely tell me something to counteract it. I feel that you say these things to counteract these feelings rather than to let me confront the difficulty directly."

This preoccupation with homosexuality subsided abruptly, however, once the more central issues were identified. It was during the third week that Margery, expressing concern about her adequacy and her psychological stability, associated these with her father who died when she was ten years old. As she talked about her father, she began to cry uncontrollably, and it soon became apparent that her relationship to him and her reaction to his death was an area of intense conflict. It also became apparent that her grief over his loss had been given no previous opportunity for expression.

For the next few weeks, the patient expressed in detail her feelings toward her father and her reaction to his death. The father had been an alcoholic and spent the last several years of his life in an institution. She described in detail the events which led to his death. She recalled how stunned she was when her uncle entered her room and announced that her father had died in the hospital. She repeated over and over again, "I just couldn't believe it." She remembered that after his death she could not think about him and wanted only to "smile and play with my friends." Her friends asked how she could possibly act the way she did when the death of her father had been so recent. For reasons she did not understand, she felt extremely guilty about his death, "as though I had somehow caused it." She became aware of the intense anger she felt towards him because of his sickness and inadequacy which necessitated his being apart from her.

As she worked on these conflicting feelings, she began to see how closely they paralleled the feeling she had toward the social worker. She realized the penchant for "falling in love with older married men who were built like and looked like Pop." The colored skin of the social worker made him appear to her like her father—handicapped and inadequate. Like her father, the social worker was also married and unattainable. The termination of the relationship with this man at the end of the summer stirred up many of the feelings she had experienced as a result of her father's death years earlier. The emptiness, the loneliness, the guilt, the self-destructiveness, and the feelings of inadequacy and helplessness were experienced with an incapacitating intensity.

As she expressed the grief that remained unexpressed for so many years, Margery realized suddenly that she was no longer preoccupied with homosexuality. She said that she did not understand why or how this particular problem was resolved, but for some reason she no longer thought about it. In addition, she mentioned that for the first time since the onset of her incapacitating symptoms one and a half years previously she had gone through a full week without experiencing an episode of depression and anxiety. She remained asymptomatic for several weeks until the question of termination of therapy came up. At this point, she once again found herself preoccupied with homosexuality and had a recurrence of her feelings of hopelessness, despair, and inadequacy. She was puzzled by this recurrence. She said that she was convinced that she had worked through her basic difficulties and was just beginning to feel elated about her progress. Now suddenly she experienced her symptoms again. It did not take long for her, however, to realize that her relationship with the therapist and the thought of separation from him were once again stirring up the feelings that brought her to him in the first place. However, this time they were considerably less incapacitating and relatively quickly resolved.

During the last hour, Margery attempted to assess her psychiatric experience and to evaluate what she had accomplished during her visits to the clinic. She said that one of the most important aspects of her therapeutic experience was having the therapist "stick with me." She said that she had feared her case would be diagnosed as a "homosexual problem" and that she would be referred elsewhere for years of therapy. She also spoke of the difficulty she had had in referring herself to the clinic, "because coming to see a psychiatrist seemed to me to confirm my feelings of inadequacy and helplessness." She said that her experience at the clinic had helped her to think about herself constructively. "I would think a lot about myself before but it was always on a very intellectual level and it left me confused. My experience here involved an emotional as well as an intellectual working through of my difficulties and thus proved very helpful." She spoke of how her psychiatric experience at the clinic aided

her in understanding "certain essential things" about herself—
especially her relationship to her father, which she felt was
the key to understanding a great deal about herself.

She attempted also to spell out how she had come to understand her inability to express her grief over her father's death
or to think about him over the years, the intense anger she
felt toward him and the feeling that she was somehow responsible for his death, her attraction to the older married social
worker as an effort to re-establish her relationship with her
father, how the termination of this relationship reactivated
the feelings occasioned by the loss of her father, and how
these feelings of worthlessness, inadequacy, and self-destruc-
tion resulted in her accusing herself of being a homosexual and
doubting her adequacy as a woman. "You see, I felt that if
homosexuality were something that I could do to myself, I
inevitably would become a homosexual."

The next problem involved helping a young man achieve an
"emotional distance" between himself and a confused and confusing family situation. Stress in the form of bereavement, conflict, dominance, and frustration was experienced all through
childhood, yet the patient's basic strengths were such that he
could endure it. Whether he would have become emotionally
decompensated (disabled with a diagnosable psychiatric entity)
during college without the help he received cannot be determined.

Bruce's decision to apply at the psychiatric clinic came after
a week of anxiety and discouragement. The step towards shar-
ing his feelings and problems with someone had been difficult
for him to take. He had become accustomed in his twenty
years of life to solving his problems by himself and he felt it
was a sign of weakness to ask for help. Yet, his attempts at
understanding and controlling his feeling on his own had confused and further depressed him. He slept in short, uneasy
snatches, was unable to concentrate on his studies, and could
not seem to sustain interest in anything about him.

Three weeks earlier he had been his usual self, as always
somewhat tired from over-study and self-pressure, but his work
was going well, he was abreast of his assignments, and was
even prepared for an impending hour exam in his biochemistry
major. If anything, he was feeling some elation at having just

received a grant for study at a western university for the next summer. He had begun to experience a feeling of progress toward his goal of taking honors in his field after two years of hard plodding. He received a first jolt when his roommate, Tom, suddenly disappeared without leaving any word of his whereabouts. Even after Tom was found at the home of a relative, Bruce still felt upset. He had not realized that Tom was troubled. He cared for Tom more than he had cared for any friend in a long time, but he had been too preoccupied with his own plans to encourage the closeness that Tom had perhaps needed. When he began to calm down he received a long distance call from his mother. She was feeling lonely and it was obvious from her rambling talk she had been drinking. She was on sick leave from her job again because of her migraine. She had become insistent that he come home for the summer and spend some time with her. She said he could pick up his old job at home in their small midwestern town. The sense of futility about his studies and his career had come after their lengthy emotional conversation. He had grudgingly given her the promise she demanded.

The telephone call had churned up many memories associated with mother's headaches and his loneliness for her when she was sick and shut away in her room. He remembered how he would wander about looking for someone with whom to play and how frightened he had been once when he strayed into a strange neighborhood looking for companions. He remembered also the rejoicing and the reunions with his mother when she felt better. Afterwards, she would shower him with attentions to the point of embarrassment. These and other old memories were examined with the psychiatrist in the ensuing weeks.

Bruce had never known his father. What he knew of him was the picture of a young Army officer on his mother's dressing table. His virtues, recited by mother, included father's family background. He came of "upper class" people, educated people, as contrasted with her own family which she labeled "lower class." Grandpa, her own father, who was a carpenter, was lower class. Mother, herself, had first married a lower class schoolmate, fresh out of high school, and had borne a daughter scarcely nine months later. That first marriage had not lasted and mother had returned to grandpa's home after her husband had disappeared. It was several years later that mother met Bruce's father. He had come to their town from Kansas to work in the engineering firm where mother was working as a clerk-typist. He was shy and lonely and reponded easily to mother's interest in him. The visit to his home in Kansas to meet his family was an exciting event for her and, although she never saw his family again, she strove in the face of their disinterest to keep in touch with them. She repeatedly told Bruce that the contacts were for his sake so that he would know the quality of his heritage. With some bitterness, she also told of his father's determination to join the service at the height of the war. She could never forgive him this decision. It hadn't been necessary for him to go. He could have stayed on with his essential war job. He had left for overseas when mother was still pregnant, and she received the news of his death a few days after Bruce's birth; but she refused to accept the report as true and kept hoping it was a mistake. Bruce was three years old before she was willing to admit to herself and to him that his father was lost.

Mother returned to grandpa's house and to her old job. Bruce grew up in a family of women. Grandpa, more enfeebled, worked only rarely. Mostly he dozed in the kitchen and, when grandma was not looking, sneaked gulps of liquor. Big sister preferred to ignore Bruce or to carry tales about him to grandma. Grandma ran the house and cared for them all, especially for mother during her attacks of migraine. To escape the oppressive atmosphere, Bruce began to wander away from home. He avoided the boys in his own neighborhood. He could not stand up to their teasing and bullying and felt himself puny in comparison to their strength. Several blocks away from home there was a Y. He had discovered it on one of his many wanderings and he had found that it contained interest clubs. There, the boys were more of his own kind, quiet, and interested in reading, and they were ready to accept him as an equal. He learned to play chess and found a new friend in Ranny, a doctor's son. Sometimes, visiting Ranny's home he was allowed to peek at the doctor's instruments and his microscope. The thought of studying medicine began to excite him and for a long time thereafter he held it as a distant goal.

When Bruce was nine, his mother made one of her spontaneous recoveries from migraine. She began to go out more, sometimes not returning until the early morning hours. She announced one evening her intentions to remarry and produced Bruce's new father-to-be. He was an Army sergeant stationed at a nearby camp. Bruce was part of the wedding party and when mother left with her new husband, Bruce went with them while big sister stayed behind with grandma and grandpa. In the next two years, Bruce moved three times as his stepfather was reassigned. His schooling was fragmentary. He shied away from the other Army children, and even his own room gave him no peace. Mother and stepfather battled and argued constantly. Stepfather drank and slammed Bruce into corners. In another sudden decision, mother bundled Bruce into a bus one night when stepfather was on duty and they returned to their old home.

Mother slid into her old ways. Now she began to sting Bruce with taunts that he would never be the man his father had been, while cursing father for having chosen his country over her. Bruce was meanwhile growing, and as he began to top his schoolmates in height, he began to be less afraid of them. He found himself being chosen for team sports. He joined the wrestling team. He discovered he had talent as an orator and as a debater. He began to read almost any book he could find to fill in the gaps in his education. He was especially interested in science fiction and dreamed of being a scientific writer. He renewed his old friendship with Ranny. He wrote after many years to his father's family and was rewarded with a warm note in reply. In his senior year in high school he found himself (to his surprise) close to the top of his class. Spurred on by his adviser, he filled out applications for colleges which he privately doubted ever would accept him.

Several colleges showed interest in him but he chose the one he had selected as his first choice. It had generously included a regular scholarship which covered most of his expenses. He supplied the necessary additional costs out of his own earnings from a summer job in the local steel plant. His savings made him feel strong and, for the first time, independent of his mother. Settling into the college life had been easier than he had expected. People were friendly and informal. Dating girls was a new and attractive experience. He felt stimulated to read in many directions and to exchange ideas with others. His first two years of college, while demanding steady application from him, were productive of a good scholastic record. In his junior year, he decided on biochemistry as a major, veering decisively away from his earlier medical dreams. He felt he was fulfilling himself. Only his relationship with his mother continued to trouble him. It seemed as though it had run progressively downhill since he entered college. His visits home soothed her but she clung to him harder than ever, each time making it more difficult for him to return to his classes.

Guided and supported by the psychiatrist, he was able to overcome the feeling that he had failed his friend as he was failing his mother. He was helped to realize that he had been successful in his long search for the kind of manly qualities his own father must have possessed. He began to see his mother's positive contribution in holding steadily up to him an image of a strong father worthy of emulation. This one facet helped to counteract the negative experiences of his life with her, and her childishly unpredictable behavior and treatment of him. He learned to feel the right to strike out on his own, away from her. By the end of the semester, he was able to restore his own life plan and to work out plans for his mother's rehabilitation in her own community.

The lack of a father with whom the son could identify figures prominently in the following history. He became overly dependent upon his mother, and when he lost her, it became apparent that he was immature in many aspects of his personality. This case is illustrative of the helpful role of a psychiatrist in aiding a young person to acquire sound ideas of the nature of independence and emotional maturation.

A twenty-year-old college student sought help for feelings of depression and loss of academic motivation early in his junior year. He was contemplating the possibility of dropping out of college for one or more terms.

His background was notable for the fact of his father's death not long after his own birth and for his being raised in a family environment which lacked the presence of any older man with whom he could form a meaningful relationship. His siblings were sufficiently older for him to enjoy an only-child status with his protective, puritanical mother. To remain in her good favor he had adopted during his growing years the role of the innocent "good boy." Her code of values stressed hard work, responsibility, and academic achievement. She had expressed criticism of the few girls in whom he had been interested. There was little joy or overt affection in the life of this incomplete family. He grew up with almost no knowledge of sex and with a paucity of experience in dating and in social life generally. In early adolescence he abandoned all religious faith owing to the stress his fundamentalist indoctrination had assigned to the sinfulness of physical pleasure. Despite these deprivations in his background he exhibited, to a surprising degree, a basically cheerful disposition (before the onset of his symptoms) and a lively and interesting personality.

About a year before he sought help his mother had died of a slowly debilitating disease. He had survived that loss without any discernible grief reaction. He had, however, greatly increased his dependency upon his roomate in an almost childish way.

The initial period of therapy brought to light the fact that his reaction to the loss of his mother was not definable in terms of his relation to her at the time but rather in terms of the more distant, early childhood relation—namely, that of his need for physical closeness and the chronic frustration of that need. Thus it was possible to approach his grief feelings only by mobilizing his emotional reaction to a much earlier loss.

Although his depression improved following the opportunity to ventilate his feelings and to form a working alliance with his therapist, he continued to struggle with the conflict of autonomy versus dependency. His continuation at college seemed in itself to express a need for passivity. By mid-year, he reached the decision to drop out for at least a semester. This decision was bolstered by his therapist, who felt that further gains could now be made in the realm of experience following this act of self-assertion. The college administrative authorities endorsed the plan even though there was no imminent threat of academic failure. (Because of his high intellectual capacity his marks had remained quite good despite his flagging interest.)

He returned to therapy the following October—seven months later—having spent the intervening time in travel and

independent study. This activity had gone far in combatting
the feeling of having been cheated out of an important phase
of his boyhood: a time that could have been spent in carefree
roving, sampling, and self-determination—had he not felt so
tied to the home. Refreshed in spirit, he was now approaching
his work with much more enthusiasm and motivation.

This second phase of therapy was geared to his continued
need for better relationships with others. Attention was paid to
his long-neglected deficiency of knowledge concerning sex and
the more "earthy" side of life. At first, he became "numb" to all
thinking on this subject, recoiling with horror from anything
suggesting "fleshly desires." Out of this essentially asexual
image of himself there gradually emerged an ability to accept
the legitimacy of his libidinal drives and a channeling of these
drives at first into conscious fantasies and later on into his
first actual involvement with a girl. Acceptance by her of his
overtures and his initiative in exploring and widening the relationship tended to correct his earlier assumption that such
behavior on his part would result in a threat to his security
(dependent attachment). He now felt much more sure of himself and experienced all the excitement of a new discovery.

Still to be worked out is the final choice of vocation following graduation, but he is working through this problem
with the psychological service in a fairly independent way.
His current preference is teaching.

Graduate students have emotional and mental disturbances
at about the same frequency as do undergraduates, but as a
rule their problems are of longer duration and even more
complex. In the following situation the major stresses occurred
in the patient's family, and in trying to deal with them he found
his own work affected. Although he developed no specific illness,
his reactions were most unpleasant, and the objective and
friendly help he received may well have prevented a tragic
outcome. The attainment of sufficient self-control to do superior
work contributed to his sense of competence and self-confidence,
and this in turn increased his ability to tolerate the adverse
developments in his family of origin.

John was a twenty-seven year old, married graduate student, who came to the clinic of his own volition because of
difficulty with his studies. He did not feel that he was failing,

but rather that he was considerably less effective than in the past. A review of his academic record indicated that he was a very bright student in grammar school and high school, and graduated in the top tenth of his class in a college of ivy league rank and quality. In graduate school, he was doing adequate but not distinguished work. He recognized that the competition was keener and the challenge greater than in college and did not expect that he would do well. Nevertheless he knew that his performance was below his usual ability. Consultation with his academic adviser confirmed this evaluation.

John grew up in a Western state in a family consisting of his father, mother, an older sister, and a younger brother. Relations between parents had been very difficult as long he could remember. Both had attended college and were well-educated. His mother was much more emotionally stable than his father. Her job as a high-level executive secretary provided the family's main source of financial support. His father had been preoccupied with alcohol for many years, frequently disappearing for days at a time and returning in a dilapidated state. On these occasions, the other members of the family helped him regain his composure, following which there ensued numerous arguments, accusations and counter-accusations between him and his wife. These episodes were very distressing to John. In recent years, deterioration in the father's appearance and behavior had become increasingly noticeable, and John had come to share his mother's hostility toward him, though he still had strong feelings of compassion for him.

For the past four years his older sister had been in and out of mental hospitals with recurrent schizophrenic episodes. The younger brother, twenty years of age, was drinking excessively, and John was quite worried about him.

John came to his first appointment appearing somewhat concerned but pleasant in manner and attractively groomed. He spoke with precision and accuracy, almost as if too well controlled. He had been married two years previously. The marriage was a successful and happy one, though both he and his wife worried a great deal about his family. He had been well accepted by her family.

His main concern was a series of new and distressing communications from his home. His father had just gone on another alcoholic binge, in the course of which he made vicious verbal attacks upon the patient's mother, as well as threatening her physically and disturbing the entire neighborhood. This upset the younger brother, who reacted by also drinking to excess. In a letter to the patient the mother stated that she was contemplating divorce, as she had many times in the past, but for the first time she had actually sought counsel from a lawyer and instituted divorce proceedings. John was concerned that if the family unit broke up the only control that had been exercised would no longer exist and he was fearful of what might happen, particularly to his younger brother. He also thought that his father would rapidly become even worse without at least the intermittent controls of the family relationship. While wondering whether or not he should return home in an attempt to reconcile his mother and father, another message came indicating that the hospitalized sister was finally well enough to be sent home for a trial visit. John greeted this news with joy as well as apprehension because he was concerned as to what might happen to his sister in the highly unstable family situation. He was very attached to her and, indeed, had been a strong and positive support to her.

Academic responsibilities seemed too pressing to permit him to make the long trip home and he decided not to go. Instead, he wrote and telephoned in an attempt to play a stabilizing role in the difficult situation. The sister was discharged from the hospital, returned home, was involved in one of the father's drunken episodes, again became disturbed and had to be returned to the hospital. Patient reported this with tears in his eyes and felt that he had been remiss in not going home, feeling that if he had gone he could somehow have prevented this recurrence of his sister's illness. The younger brother disappeared from home after writing to the patient that he could not "take it" any longer and that he was going to go off on his own in an attempt to work things out. At the time of the sister's return from the hospital, his mother halted legal proceedings in the hope that the family's concern for the sick daughter would somehow pull things together and that even the father might react supportively to this new crisis. When the sister was returned to the hospital the mother immediately re-instituted legal proceedings, the divorce was granted, and the father disappeared.

Except for transient anxiety and mild depression, the patient seemed to be dealing with this complicated and difficult life situation in a mature fashion. Psychological testing, done at the height of the family distress, showed that the patient was rigid and detail-oriented, solving problems by obsessively marshaling all the details and facts. He seemed to have difficulty in making the inferential jump from the evidence to a conclusion; nor was he very flexible. The number of his approaches to problem-solving situations was limited and he had trouble shifting from them to meet new and unexpected challenges. Nevertheless, the overall testing material showed the patient to be in reasonably good shape. There was no evidence of any notable psychopathology. He appeared to be neither a schizophrenic nor a psychopathic deviate, the two mental conditions he feared he might be developing. He worried about himself in various ways. He spent much time musing about his position in the world. At the same time, there was evidence that the patient's emotional defenses were effective. Most of the time he was relatively unimpaired in his functioning.

In the course of two months of psychotherapy at weekly intervals, the patient was able to resume near-normal functioning. Treatment was devoted almost entirely to identification of the patient's hostility toward his father and guilt for his "neglect" of his siblings, particularly the older sister. The opportunity to ventilate his concerns, to clarify the issues in his life, particularly with regard to the limits of his responsibility to other members of his family, was sufficient to allow him to move ahead and to regain his capacity to work. He completed his first year of graduate work with a creditable record. Even though the family situation was essentially unchanged, he did academic work of a superior quality during his second year.

Delayed emotional maturation due to unsatisfying relations with his parents is the theme of the next history. The fact that so many of the emotional difficulties of college as well as graduate students have their origin in family discord or lack of suitable figures for emulation causes parents to become defensive. They may feel that those who describe the effects of unsatisfying relations of children with their parents are not sympathetic with their problems. Parents should not be blamed for their children's emotional conflicts but helped to understand why they arose. The therapist's task is to help students understand their parents as well as their own reactions to them and, when possible, to strengthen family ties.

Toward the end of his first year, a twenty-six-year-old graduate school student referred himself for psychiatric consultation. He was rather vague about his reasons for seeking help. A "platonic" girl friend had recently told him that he always seemed to be trying to impress people rather than to be his natural self. This caused the student to reflect about his past and to realize how insecure and inferior he had felt for many years. It was following this, he told the therapist, that he decided to come in for a conference "because you were so handy." His comment that he "would like to see myself as others see me—to find out what I am really like" revealed a lack of objectivity in terms of self-awareness. He had never been able to confide in anyone, including himself.

This young man of medium-heavy build presented a pleasant personality and seemed quite composed in his emotional reactions. There was a certain flexibility about him which was in part reflected in suggestibility. One of the most striking things about him was the tendency to be suprised by little discoveries about his own reactions in the process of simply talking about himself. This tendency was quite analogous to the process of spontaneous associations generated by certain patients in the course of verbalizing the manifest content of a dream.

His past history was notable chiefly for the fact of his parents' divorce during his early adolescent years, an anemic relationship with a rather withdrawn father, and a long subordination to a protective and managerial mother. His mother often deprecated her bachelor brother as well as her husband in terms of "the men they could have been." The patient was the youngest of three siblings, brought up in a large city. Before the divorce took place his mother often threatened to leave, never quite indicating for sure whether she would take the patient with her. He used to fear privately that he would not live to be ten years old and suffered great anxiety on the eve of that birthday, as he did again at the self-suggested milestones of thirteen and twenty-one. His high school and college years were not especially eventful. Though he went out for a few sports, he could never achieve much proficiency. His coaches often remarked that he seemed to be "holding back." He was plagued by minor injuries which would temporarily keep him from participating. His dating with girls was somewhat delayed because of shyness and lack of sophistication. These relationships tended to remain focused upon the more superficial, physical aspects. He worked for several years with a large engineering firm prior to enrolling in graduate school. Although this satisfied some of his needs for security, he fancied himself some day working in a more independent way—possibly in business for himself.

During the six interviews which took place before the school year was completed, he made remarkable gains in seeing a side of himself which had long been overshadowed by caution, reserve, inhibition, and self-doubt. Very quickly he developed insight into the origin of these traits in his passive compliance with his parents' expectations of him. He came to see what sacrifice he had made in this compliance and, guided to a consideration of his own expectations of himself, was able to achieve a much better awareness of his assets and capabilities. This advance was reflected in his performance on his final exams which was considerably better than on previous occasions in terms of organization, free flow of ideas, and even spelling.

By the time he left to start his summer job he was enjoying a new-found sense of freedom, a restored confidence, and a drive toward accomplishment and self-expression. "I feel as though I have got back inside myself rather than trying to look at myself from the outside."

Five months later he returned, reporting that these previous gains had been maintained during a successful job experience during the summer. The residue of conflict was now centered around what seemed to be an obsessive drive to be married. During a few more interviews he was able to become more sharply aware of the subtle pressure which had long been exerted upon him by his mother to find the right girl and to be married early. (She had misrepresented her age on her own marriage license because she felt so ashamed that she had not married until her middle twenties!) On the other hand, she was critical of those girls whom he had brought home for her to meet. In fact, his engagement to a girl had been broken about two years previously because of this kind of disapproval. He came to the realization that his rush to be married was actually a defensive means of concealing from himself his distrust of an entangling relationship. His insight into the nature of this distrust (his unconscious selection of a woman who would once again dominate him) was followed by a change in his object choice. Thus there emerged a preference for a girl whom he could lead, instead of his previous attraction to a more aggressive personality. This change paralleled his earlier improvement in feelings of worth and self-confidence.

Faculty members, too, have problems. The following case illustrates how supportive treatment, in the form of crisis intervention, may enable an individual to withstand much personal stress and yet work effectively. I am continually amazed, after thirty years of work in institutions of higher learning, at how many faculty members carry extremely heavy psychological burdens and are yet able to do distinguished work. Everyone has serious emotional problems; any individual may encounter a series of adverse circumstances which may temporarily overtax his ability to deal with them. Skillful help at such times of crisis may be the most important work the college psychiatrist can do.

A thirty-five-year-old man who was attending a summer engineering institute requested psychiatric consultation soon after his enrollment. He was a professor of electrical engineering at a midwestern university which had sponsored him for this special program in research methods.

His concern was a marital problem which had existed for more than a year but which had recently become intensified when his wife, shortly after his arrival at the college, notified him that she was instituting divorce proceedings. They had been married for 15 years and their two boys were now aged ten and twelve respectively. His immediate reaction to receiving this news was to think of and to plan ways in which he might commit suicide. He did not specify his plan, merely hinting that it would be violent but carried out at a time and place which would not inconvenience or embarrass anyone. He maintained that he felt nothing but love for his wife and wished to provide for her happiness. She had long complained of his conservative and possessive attitude as being a restraint upon the gay and active social life she desired. For over ten years he had been suffering from an incurable disease but had been able to control it and to extend his life beyond expectancy by adhering to a rather specifically antagonistic drug. He tended to justify his prospective act of suicide by maintaining that it would liberate his wife from him while she was still reasonably young and capable of attracting another man.

A flurry of long distance calls just before he consulted the college psychiatrist had resulted in a compromise by which both agreed to seek psychological evaluation (and treatment if indicated). Her referral was to be expedited by their minister, whom they had seen separately and together from time to time in the earlier phase of the marital discord.

During the ensuing weeks at the college he continued to report for frequent (and at times daily) interviews, although he denied the need for help or for change in his attitude. He was able to ventilate some of his feelings concerning the loss of many comrades during World War II in both the European and Pacific combat areas, but could not see the relevance of those losses to his chronically depressive outlook nor to the threat of loss in the current situation. When he learned from his wife that she had received a "clean bill of health" from her evaluating psychiatrist and that she was again resolved to press the suit for divorce, he renewed his suicidal intentions, but now in a manner which might not be suspected of being self-inflicted: he would simply stop taking his life-sustaining medication. Thus he would avoid the appearance of "a cowardly threat or gesture of suicide" which was his wife's interpretation of his previously declared intention.

During the last few weeks of his program he was gradually brought to realize the importance to him of his two sons and his responsibility to them. It was also possible to mobilize some of the strong feelings of anger toward his wife which had previously been contained behind his grim attitude of self-sacrifice. By the time he left to return home he had relented to the extent that he was willing at least to consider some more constructive alternative courses of action. Despite the severity of his depression he had been able to attend all of his classes and had performed satisfactorily in the academic program.

Several months later a follow-up letter from his minister indicated that this man and his wife were proceeding with the divorce action, that he was again taking his medication, and had returned to his job. The minister felt that psychiatric intervention had "provided the turning point" in a protracted crisis.

Two years later another report told of his continued good adjustment to his work and a positive relationship with his boys whom he saw quite regularly.

Women students have many of the same problems as the men display, but some are characteristic of them because of their dependent relationship with men and their concerns about marriage or a career. Some young women can function well at colleges with low academic standing but will develop symptoms, sometimes of an ominous nature (schizophrenic break), when they attempt to meet the academic demands of those colleges of highest standing. Suicidal gestures are not uncommon and should always be taken seriously and investigated thoroughly. Sometimes they call for removal from college, sometimes not. Depression is a common presenting symptom in young women. They may worry excessively and experience feelings of futility, sadness, loneliness, and worthlessness. They cannot work effectively, concentration is impossible, and they suffer from examination anxiety. Many of them suffer temporarily because they have been thrust into situations that require all their abilities before they have acquired self-mastery.

Some of them use quite inappropriate devices to cope with anxiety or depression. Suicidal attempts, personal slovenliness, over-eating, premature sexual experimentation, and excessive and compulsive studying are among the signs that help is urgently needed. Much can be done in even a few interviews to help them deal with their guilt, oppression, and self-defeatism.

In women graduate students anxiety and depression are usually more prolonged, and the neurotic defenses are more organized. They must work under tension, often with inadequate financial backing. Many of them are unmarried and worried about it while the men with whom they are frequently associated are married or unmarriageable.

Among both male and female graduate students the incidence of acute emotional disorder is no higher than among undergraduates, but the severity appears to be greater.

Since much of the literature on the emotional conflicts of college students has come from those institutions with relatively large psychiatric services, and these are mainly in the residential colleges, the impression has often been conveyed that those students who go to these colleges are more unstable than those students who go to commuter colleges. Recently, Kysar[5] of the Chicago Undergraduate Division of the University of Illinois, has expressed the opposite opinion. As a result of five years of experience in treating students in that institution, he has come to the tentative conclusion that the psychiatric problems of the urban commuter student differ in type, severity, and frequency from the problems of students in residential colleges. He found that many of his student patients suffered from feelings of social and sexual inadequacy, over-control of their impulses resulting in preoccupation with their studies as an essential defense, fear of failure with strong desires to avoid significant commitment to anything, isolation and indecision resulting in inner emptiness and outer isolation, and over-dependency and conformity to parents' expectations. He found a high proportion of parents who viewed college as vocational training; it was a threat to a cherished way of life yet essential to social and economic success. Kysar also suggests that the parents of commuter students have a higher incidence of problems of their own than do the parents of residential students.

REFERENCES

1. HARRISON, R. W.: Leaving college because of emotional problems. In: *Psychosocial Problems of College Men*, B. M. Wedge, Ed. New Haven, Yale, 1958, pp. 95-112.
2. CARMEN, L. R.: A three-to-five-year study of thirty-five psychotic hospitalized students, *J. Amer. Coll. Health Ass.*, *13*:541-550, 1965.
3. LANGSLEY, P. R., KAMMERER, B., AND POPE, S.: Acute psychosis in a college population: Acute psychotic reaction. Psychiatric

Research Report No. 16, American Psychiatric Association, 1963, pp. 36-48.

4. WALTERS, P. A., JR.: Student apathy. *Emotional Problems of the Student,* In: G. B. Blaine, Jr., and C. C. McArthur, Eds. New York, Appleton, 1961, pp. 153-171.

5. KYSAR, J. E.: Mental health in an urban commuter university. *Arch. Gen. Psychiat. (Chicago),* *11*:472-483, 1964.

CHAPTER V

SUICIDE

M OTIVES FOR SUICIDE and means of accomplishing it are almost as varied as human being themselves. Regarding the act, its perpetrators, and its prevention there are no set rules, although one principle is fundamental: anyone who talks about committing suicide must be taken seriously. Distinctions between a manipulative gesture and a genuine threat are to some extent spurious because the admitted contemplation indicates emotional difficulty and a need for help; furthermore, the stakes are too high to allow risks in the name of educated guesses.

The number of people who consider such a move is many times greater than the number who attempt it, and the number who attempt it is several times greater than the number who succeed. For obvious reasons the exact figures are unknown but estimates frequently range from six to ten attempts for every completed suicide.

Suicide does not necessarily indicate the existence of psychosis. Extreme unhappiness or discouragement may occur in the absence of mental illness, i.e., as a response to external events. Many suicides are associated with isolation and with vocational failure. The suicide rate is relatively high among the widowed, the economically underprivileged, the aged, the unmarried, and physicians—the latter presumably because of the ease of obtaining agents.

The mental illness which chiefly causes suicide is depression. Usually the depressed individual has strong feelings of hostility towards others which are deflected inwards; often the mechanism chosen tends to express that hostility. Most potential suicides furnish clues to their intentions. Suicide in adults is not usually an impulsive spur-of-the-moment act, but instead represents the culmination of a long-standing disturbance. Investigation of an individual's life prior to his suicide usually reveals evidences of severe conflict. It is not uncommon for a previously depressed, recently improved person to take his life. This occurs because he still has morbid ideas and has not yet gained full control of himself; his increasing energies permit destructive mobilization.

The most effective protection against suicide is a warm personal relationship between the suicidal person and others who care for him. Thus it is vital that a college administration or faculty be able to acquaint itself with troubled students—or at least be readily accessible to them—and establish therapeutic contact. This must be done without panic but with obvious evidence of general concern for each individual's difficulties.

For more than 50 years suicide has been one of the leading causes of death in the United States. During the past few years there has been an increase in suicide for all ages but particularly for adolescents and young adults. (See Table I.) The increase is greater among non-whites than in the white population.

TABLE I*
AVERAGE OF ANNUAL DEATH RATES PER 100,000

Age Period (Years)	Males 1950-52	1960-62	Increase	Females 1950-52	1960-62	Increase
			White			
All ages	16.9	17.5	4%	4.9	5.5	12%
15-19	4.0	5.9	48%	1.7	1.7	0
20-24	9.4	11.8	26%	3.0	3.5	17%
			Non-white			
Colleges	7.4	9.1	23%	1.7	2.4	41%
15-19	1.9	3.5	84%	1.3	1.6	23%
20.24	8.3	11.1	34%	2.3	2.9	26%

* Metropolitan Life Insurance Co., *Statistical Bulletin*, Vol. 45, July 1964, pp. 8, 9 & 10.

In the general population, firearms are the leading instrument for suicide, followed by poisoning, hanging, and strangulation. More than 20,000 suicides are recorded each year in the United States. There is a far greater number of unsuccessful attempts. In addition, many suicides are reported as accidental deaths. It is estimated that nearly two million people now living in the United States have attempted suicide at least once.

Jacobziner recently reviewed the available data regarding

suicide during adolescence.[1] He notes that adolescent suicide is increasing both in absolute numbers and in importance as deaths from other causes decline. In 1962, 659 of the individuals who committed suicide were less than twenty years of age; one was only seven years old. In the entire group, 499 were male and 160 female. In nearly 50 per cent of the cases, jumping from high places was the method. Hanging and strangulation were the next most common methods, almost always in males. Suicide ranks fourth as a cause of death in the fifteen to nineteen age group. Jacobziner's study of all the suicidal attempts in New York City in 1960-61 individuals between twelve and 20 years of age who used chemicals as the method reveals that 597 confirmed attempts were made, the ratio of attempts to successes being more than 100 to 1. Family disorganization was high in the group of attempted suicides. Reasons given by the individuals who did not succeed were quarrels with family, relatives, friends; depression; school difficulty; and impaired interpersonal relations with members of the opposite sex. Aspirin, barbiturates, and tranquilizing drugs were the usual chemical agents employed.

In this adolescent group, a suicidal gesture was often a sudden precipitous reaction (in contrast to the experience with adults) to a stressful situation resulting from frustration, depression, anger, or as a rebellious act against some restraining person, usually one who was loved. The individuals seemed to want to frighten or warn the persons responsible for them of their unhappiness with present conditions. Would-be suicides were higher in deprived areas. A high percentage of the adolescents who attempted suicide came from unstable and disorganized homes; feelings of insecurity, frustration, depression, being unwanted and alone, and a lack of sympathy, understanding, and someone to listen to their difficulties were common.

Although suicidal attempts in adolescents are frequently of an impulsive nature, and the reasons for them temporary (rather than a determined wish to die), they may succeed due to a miscalculation by the individual or delay in obtaining prompt and appropriate treatment.

Bruyn and Seiden studied suicide at the University of California at Berkeley from 1952 to 1961 inclusive.[2] The rate was 17.44 per 100,000 compared to a total statewide suicide rate of 16.01 per 100,000. Among the Berkeley students, accidents were the leading cause of death (37%) and suicides second (34%). As they point out, one could say that students die of little else than accidents and suicide.

In summary, their findings indicate that the suicide rate is slightly higher among college students than in the rest of the State of California, whereas the general mortality experience of college students is more favorable than those outside colleges. They found no evidence of an increased incidence of suicide in the University; the increased number merely kept pace with the increase in general population.

As at other institutions with adequate psychiatric services, Berkeley is much concerned about early diagnosis and treatment, an effective network of communication among all who have responsibility for students, making people in the community alert to the signs of suicide, and intense therapeutic efforts when a suicidal person is found. They see a direct connection between the emotional health of the individual student and the total emotional health of the community.

Murphy compared student suicides in the Far East and in this country, stating that in the United States if a student threatens suicide this means that he will probably do it whether he fails in college or not, but in India this view is not tenable. Year after year, as he says, there is a genuine wave of suicides after examination results come out. Murphy also says that suicide rates differ depending on the background. For instance, the South Indians and the Ceylonese Tamil speak the same language and are of similar appearance and identical origin but the suicide rate in the Ceylonese group is several times higher than in the South Indian group.[3]

The study of Parnell of suicide at Oxford, published in 1951, indicated that in the three-year period, 1947 to 1949, the suicide rate was eleven times that of the general population age fifteen to twenty-four.[4]

Diehl and Sheppard studied the causes of death in 327 students from nine universities who died in the ten-year period from

1925 to 1935. They found that suicide accounted for 8 per cent of this group, being exceeded by heart and circulatory diseases and accidents.[5]

In a study of Yale University students, Parrish found that twenty-five (12 per cent) of 209 deaths during the years 1920 to 1955 inclusive were due to suicide. It was second only to accidents as a leading cause of death in the student population. During this period, there was one suicide for every 6,956 student-years. Only eleven of the twenty-five students who committed suicide had been seen by psychiatrists in the Department of Mental Hygiene and Psychiatry.

Parrish was unable to determine any particular constellation of factors that would predict suicide accurately. The intellectual level of the group was about the same as that of the University generally. Only one had a serious physical problem, a duodenal ulcer which was asymptomatic at the time of his death. In only five of the students was there evidence of a drop in grades. Financial stress was present in eight of the twenty-five. Sexual difficulties were present in six.[6]

Pope and Wheelright stated that the suicide rate at the University of California in 1956 was about three a year. They said that none had been known to the Health Service at the University of Utah.[7]

In Temby's analysis of suicides at Harvard University from 1935 to 1957, he states that there is no "suicidal personality," nor any easily recognizable sign to indicate that a student is going to commit suicide. Sometimes the first indication of a student's difficulty is his body's being found after a successful attempt. However, of the twenty-six cases from 1946 to 1959, premonitory acts, symptoms, or personality changes were noticed by friends, family, or teachers shortly before the suicide. There is no particular time of the year, or year in the undergraduate period or in graduate school, in which suicides are apt to be more frequent than at any other time. Religious affiliation did not seem to have any bearing on suicide. Suicide by contagion, that is by reading the details of a suicide at another college, is frequent enough in the experience of health directors that they all wish publicity could be avoided, especially as to details. At Harvard, the rate went down very markedly during the war years. There is no correlation with academic standing although preoccupation with grades was common. In twenty-five of the thirty-five suicides reported by Temby, there was some evidence of pre-existing emotional illness, usually a depression. Fourteen had a definite history of gross psychological symptomatology; sixteen could be said to be depressed. In only two cases was it known beforehand by medical authorities that suicide was on the student's mind. Temby warns that anything that a student says while talking about suicide should be taken seriously, not only in spirit but in letter. Even jokes about it may be significant.[8]

Temby's report on suicides at Harvard University extended through the academic year 1958-59. In the following six years (1959-65), there were seven known suicides, the methods used being hanging in three cases and firearms and barbiturates, two cases each. Two of these occurred after treatment had begun, one of them after hospitalization away from the University, one during transfer from treatment in the Health Services to longer-term treatment in a hospital clinic. Five of the suicides were students who had not been known to have any emotional problems. Postmortem investigation revealed evidence of considerable emotional turmoil in each of these, but the students had not elected to seek help.

The average enrollment of the University during the twelve years from 1946 to 1957 in which there were twenty-six suicides was 10,511, a total of 132,437 student years with one suicide for every 5,090 student years. During the seven-year period from 1958 to 1965 there were nine suicides, the average annual enrollment was 13,515, a total of 94,604 student years, and one suicide for every 10,511 student years or about 9.5 per 100,000 (slightly lower than the national average). This represents a reduction in mortality from suicide of approximately 51 per cent.

One often hears statements in the public press and on radio or TV concerning the alarming increase in suicide among college students. The evidence for such statements is unavailable to me.

In order to maintain comparability of records, any student who commits suicide while in the University or during the same academic year following a medical leave of absence is counted in our series. If a depressed student were to withdraw from the University in May or June and commit suicide during the course of his illness, even though it were the end of the academic year, he would be counted.

For the college psychiatrist (and the whole college as well) the suicide of a student is the most dreaded of all the developments that can affect him. Its irreversibility, the bewildering variety of motivations for it, its dramatic nature in many instances, and the retrospective awareness that it might not have happened if any one of several dozen things had been done differently, all combine to produce frustration.

Even though suicide of a patient is always a distressing event to the psychiatrist caring for him, no matter what the circumstances, the loss of a college student is especially tragic. The individual is nearly always young, and if it could have been prevented the probability is that he would have lived a long and valuable life. A college suicide, particularly when attended by publicity, often seems to suggest to some other student, often hundreds of miles away, that he should end his own life in a similar way. Futhermore, the episode is a traumatic one to his colleagues.

An aspect of suicide that is infrequently considered, and about which no absolute conclusions can be drawn, is the use of this measure as a threat by disturbed persons to achieve something very much desired at the moment or to prevent some undesirable event. Some examples:

A parent who threatens suicide unless an abortion is performed on his unmarried pregnant daughter;

A student who has been given a medical leave of absence from college but who insists he will take his own life unless the decision is rescinded;

A professor who fears a student will commit suicide unless he gives him a passing grade in his course;

A student who threatens to kill himself when his connections with his college are severed;

A student who, after hospitalization for a depression with suicidal attempts, states emphatically that he will kill himself unless discharged;

A student who calls his girl friend, telling her that unless she will respond affirmatively to his advances he will use the lethal weapons which he has beside him as he talks (gun, bottle of whisky, bottle of pills, knife, etc.).

There is no limit to the variety of methods by which emotionally disturbed persons may try to attain what they want. The worst thing that could be done is to respond to such threats by giving in to the demands. Whatever decisions are thought to be right and proper should be made; the person who makes the unreasonable demands must be handled gently and fairly but with the important fact that *he is a disturbed person* clearly in mind. Most of those who use suicidal threats in this manner are aggressive and usually hostile to someone (hostility directed outwardly); hence the risk of their taking impulsive self-destructive action is not high. These people are usually desperate. They need help badly. Their suicidal threats are the most dramatic way by which they can make their desperation known. They will usually respond to efforts to help and to understand them. For example, in the cases referred to above, all but one responded favorably and did constructive work afterward, in some instances quite distinguished work. The exception was the student who demanded his release under threat of suicide. His request was granted, following which he promptly tried again and succeeded.

Barbiturates and sedatives are often used in suicidal attempts, but usually a considerable number of capsules or pills must be ingested to be lethal. This reduces the possibility that completed suicides by drugs result from confusion or "accident." Acquiring a sufficient amount of sedatives is comparatively easy for a clever person determined to end his life, but is not so easy for most depressed and confused young men and women who may act on impulse. This suggests that all physicians and nurses in college health services should be constantly alert to detect the disturbed persons who are trying to collect enough sedatives for a suicidal attempt. If a physician has repeated requests for "sleeping pills," he should prescribe them in small amounts, authorize no refills, make appropriate notations in the health record which show caution but which do not reflect on the patient; if he is in doubt about the reason for a particular person's urgency of manner, he should consult the college psychiatrist.

In large health services, internists and psychiatrists, in the effort
to maintain their patients' privacy, may not know that a patient
has consulted more than one physician. This can happen easily
when psychiatric records are kept separate from the general
medical records, as they should be.[9]

When a suicide does occur in a college, a public relations problem always arises. The public relations officer of the college
and the high administrative officials under whose jurisdiction the
student has been should be notified immediately. Parents or
next of kin also must be notified at once; if this can be done by
the college official or teacher who knows him best, followed by
a conference, by telephone or in person, with the physician, the
family can usually get the maximum information in a short time.
In many cases the proof of suicide may not be absolute; family
members should not be deprived of their doubts nor of their hopes
that their child might not have intended to take his own life.

Newspapers are, of course, always interested in dramatic news,
and suicides are quite newsworthy from their point of view. On
the other hand, the feelings of the family and concern for the
memory of the deceased require the gentlest possible treatment
of such news. Good personal relations between the public relations officer of the college and reporters and publishers in the
community, together with similar good relations between the
director of the health service and reporters and editors of the
college newspaper, may determine whether reports of such deaths
are handled with dignity or with disrespect. In any case, statements by the college should always be disseminated through the
public relations officer (or head of news bureau) to avoid
misunderstandings or tactlessness.

Any psychiatric program which has as its primary goal the
prevention of all suicides among the population for which it is
responsible will cause more suicides than it prevents. When
extreme "suicide precautions" are observed strictly and impersonally, the rate of suicide among patients may indeed be low
but the amount of needless frustration and interference with
treatment designed to get patients back into their own communities is great. Like the pursuit of happiness, the prevention
of suicide should be a secondary, not the primary, goal. Principal
emphasis should be placed on the development of early case-

finding, prompt and adequate treatment, alerting of all key associates to the possibility of suicide, and maintenance of open lines of communication between the patient and someone whom he respects and in whom he has confidence.

This latter principle was impressed on the writer many years ago while caring for a college freshman who began to show signs of an acute agitated depression but without any overt suicidal tendencies. The patient was requested to come to the office or call on the telephone if he had any thoughts about or impulses toward taking any drastic action of which he did not approve. One Sunday morning he appeared at the college infirmary; he had gone to a high cliff a few miles from the college to end his life by jumping over it, when he remembered his promise. He was promptly hospitalized, responded to treatment, returned to college and was graduated, served four years in the armed forces during World War II (with much combat duty), completed professional training soon thereafter, and has since practiced his profession with distinction.

The lessons taught by this case have been reinforced throughout the succeeding years in clinical practice with college students:

(1) Suspect suicidal preoccupations or actions in anyone who is depressed and anxious.

(2) Make it clear to the patient (but in a tactful manner) that he is free to talk about his feelings without precipitous action being taken to restrict his freedom.

(3) Develop a warm and accepting yet objective relation with the patients suspected of suicidal ruminations.

(4) Keep lines of communication open at all times from him to a source of help.

(5) The prognosis of persons contemplating suicide may be, and usually is, quite good if appropriate treatment is obtained.

(6) Some risk-taking by the college psychiatrist is always necessary. Consultation by the person who has the primary responsibility with other key officials is usually desirable. This may include talking with the Dean of Students, the President (especially in small colleges), a professional colleague who may be able to take a more objective view. Parents of minors, or the next of kin, should usually be informed if suicidal signs become ominous.

Incorrect ideas about suicide continue to circulate among those with little or no experience with the phenomenon. People who talk about suicide often *do* attempt it, and many succeed. There usually are warning signs if only they can be interpreted properly. Patients *do* commit suicide impulsively when they appear to be improving. All suicides are *not* among depressed or psychotic people. Suicide is not a disease but a method of dealing with an infinite number of seemingly insoluble problems. It is not immoral. It is not inherited. It cannot be controlled by legislation. It occurs at all age levels and in all socioeconomic groups.[10]

REFERENCES

1. JACOBZINER, H.: Attempted suicides in adolescence. *J.A.M.A., 191*:7-11, 1965.
2. BRUYN, H. B., AND SEIDEN, R. H.: Student suicide: fact or fancy? *J. Amer. Coll. Health Ass.* In press.
3. MURPHY, H. B. M.: In: *The Student and Mental Health: An International View,* D. H. Funkenstein, Ed. New York, World Federation for Mental Health, 1959, pp. 194-206.
4. PARNELL, R. W.: Mortality and prolonged illness among Oxford undergraduates. *Lancet, CCLX*:731, 1951.
5. DIEHL, H. S., AND SHEPARD, C. E.: *The Health of College Students.* Washington, D. C., Amer. Council Education, 1939, p. 100.
6. PARRISH, H. N.: Epidemiology of suicide among college students. *Yale J. Biol. Med., 29*:585-595, 1957.
7. POPE, S., AND WHEELRIGHT, J. B.: In: *The Student and Mental Health: An International View.* D. H. Funkenstein, Ed. New York, World Federation for Mental Health, 1959, pp. 449-450.
8. TEMBY, W. D.: In: *Emotional Problems of the Student,* G. B. Blaine, and C. C. McArthur, Eds. New York, Appleton, 1961, pp. 133-152.
9. FARNSWORTH, D. L., Ed.: *College Health Administration.* New York, Appleton, 1964, p. 73.
10. FARBEROW, N. L., AND SHNEIDMAN, E. S., Eds.: *The Cry for Help.* New York, McGraw-Hill, 1961, pp. 13-14.

CHAPTER VI

DROPOUTS

T HE HIGH RATE OF withdrawal from college has received so much attention by educators and reporters who write on educational problems that many people have assumed that it is a new problem. The "dropout" rate, as it has come to be called, has been high in schools and colleges for many years. There is no evidence that it is increasing. The present concern about the situation may well be due to our increasing need for more skilled and educated persons than we have; a reduction in the rate of attrition would be an attractive solution to the manpower shortage, as well as a means of increasing the low income of many families and thus one means of attacking the problem of poverty. In addition, since a higher percentage of our young people are now attending college, the disadvantages of not doing so are greater than they were when only a few high school graduates continued their formal educations.

Those who fail to complete their college programs cause great concern to their parents, to college financial officers, and to those concerned with college public relations. Each individual who leaves prematurely is, of course, seriously troubled or disappointed. Many students leave precipitously for reasons which are never ascertained.

Summerskill has recently reviewed the studies that have been concerned with this problem during the period from 1913 to 1962. During this time the number of those who failed to graduate from the college they entered was remarkably steady, usually about 60 per cent.[1] McNeely studied 15,535 students in 1931-32 and found that 62.1 per cent left college, 17 per cent went to other institutions, but that there was a net loss to higher education of 45.2 per cent of the total.[2] In a 1958 study, Iffert found that in his sample of 13,700 students entering college in 1950, 39.5 per cent were graduated from the college they entered. He estimated that 59 per cent ultimately were graduated at some institution.[3] In the thirty-five studies reviewed by Summerskill, the median percentage of loss was 50 per cent in four years, while the median percentage who were graduated from their own institutions in four years was 37 per cent. Attrition was usually greater in state universities than in private colleges. There was no significant difference in the rates for men and women. Rates tended to be higher among students who came from rural areas. Good grades in secondary schools decreased the probability of dropping out. Other factors increasing the probability of withdrawal included lack of values favorable to education, poor motivation, low scores on intelligence and college board tests, and parental conflict, especially when a career choice was being forced on a student. Those who had a "doing" orientation toward education did poorly in "being" oriented colleges.

Whereas the reasons for leaving college were formerly sought mainly in terms of institutional and administrative difficulties, the recent trend is toward the elucidation of psychological and sociological causes. Even in the colleges with the highest standards of selection, about 20 to 25 per cent of the members of each entering class fail to graduate in four years; very few of those who drop out do so because of lack of intelligence, but rather because of inability or unwillingness to bring intellectual capacity to bear on studies. Summerskill asserts that "the attrition problems that predominate in the colleges involve the students' failure to meet the psychological, sociological, or economic demands rather than the strictly academic demands of the college environment."[4] In specific terms, the factors related to withdrawal from college are those of motivation, adjustment, illness or injury, and finances. Interpersonal conflict in families, marked disparity between value systems of home and college environment, identity crises, and problems of sexual maturation occur with great frequency among those who are unable to work effectively.

Pervin has recently reported on the results of his long-term study of students who withdrew from Princeton University in the classes which entered in 1936, 1947, and 1956. He picked these classes because they were relatively unaffected by economic depressions or war. A dropout was defined as someone who had officially withdrawn, regardless of the reason, and thus did not get his degree in four years. Cooperation with his study was much greater from students who had not withdrawn than from those who had done so. He found that the percentage who had withdrawn from Princeton had not changed since the Class of 1940, but a higher proportion of recent classes were considering such action. About 20 per cent of all students entering Princeton drop out at some time. The reasons for their dropping out, however, have changed considerably. More people in the later class dropped out for personal and health reasons as opposed to required reasons (that is, academic and disciplinary).

About three-quarters of those who withdrew in the Class of 1940 did so because they were required to withdraw, whereas only about half of those leaving in the latter two classes withdrew for that reason. Pervin found a fairly even distribution of dropouts over the course of the four years. The difference in intellectual capacity between those who withdrew and those who did not is slowly disappearing. Academic ability alone does not play a significant part in determining who drops out. Uncertainty as to choice of course and career was very noticeable in those who withdrew. In the first class (1940), about 50 per cent of the dropouts returned to college; in the Class of 1951, 82 per cent returned; in the Class of 1960, 77 per cent returned. Of those who did return, 53 per cent in the Class of 1940 got their degrees; 74 per cent, in the Class of 1951; and 80 per cent, in the Class of 1960. The latter figure indicates that a student returning to college after having dropped out has a higher probability of obtaining his degree than a student first entering college.

In investigating the incomes of those who withdrew and those who did not, the incomes of those who remained in college has been consistently higher than those who withdrew. Divorce rates were higher in those who had withdrawn than those who had not. Those who withdrew because of being required to do so in general had more difficulty and less reward for the work they performed than did those who withdrew on their own. A general tentative conclusion drawn from all of this is that the majority of students in this group who did drop out were able to make satisfactory academic, vocational, and personal adjustments in later life. As one professor stated, dropping out may be an inefficient but effective way of getting an education.[5]

Ford and Urban suggest that it should not always be inferred that students who leave college represent a loss of potential talent to our society. It might be plausibly argued that such students are moving toward more effective use of their talents when they drop out and thus represent a benefit to our society rather than a loss. In any case, the possibilities of both loss and benefit should be considered; some of those who leave college may be making constructive moves, given their circumstances and state of mind.

Those students whose aptitudes, interests, personal characteristics, and career objectives are best developed in a college environment, and who are forced by reasons beyond their control to lapse into life patterns less appropriate and satisfying to them, do represent a waste of talent, time, and money for both the student and the college. But those students have been poorly advised, Ford and Urban assert, "who are coaxed and wheedled into going away to college—youngsters who are not academically oriented; who do not learn well under the circumstances provided by the typical university with its highly formalized system of abstract instruction, course requirements, credit structures, and the like; or whose career aspirations actually call for an entirely different kind of background than that provided by our colleges and universities. For students such as these, the decision to leave college may represent a constructive act, a step toward a more productive, meaningful life."

This differentiation suggests that one of the precautions that should be kept in mind by those extolling the virtues of attendance at college is that careers attainable by other routes than a college education should not be downgraded. Undoubtedly, as the proportion of young people attending college increases, the negative social pressures on those who do not will increase. How to maintain as much respect for the accomplishment of those not formally educated as those who go to college is as yet an unsolved problem; at least, most parents who approve of college themselves feel strongly that their children should go to college.

Ford and Urban maintain that any college or university that chooses to do so can markedly reduce the number of its students who drop out (unless that number is already quite small). To do this the institution should collect and correlate data regarding the admission, academic performance, related characteristics of its students and accomplishments of those who drop out and those who graduate, and evaluate the results of its educational efforts and discover those aspects of its operation which should be improved. Since their institution has begun such a program, including effective counseling, the number of students placed on the dean's list has increased dramatically, while the number of those dropped for low scholarship has decreased equally impressively.[6]

Peszke and Arnstein have reported that approximately 25 per cent of Yale undergraduates do not finish on time (same as Harvard). Those who leave for psychiatric reasons usually do not have as good a record upon their return as other students. About 80 per cent of all returnees were graduated, while about 66 per cent of all who leave for emotional or mental illness were eventually graduated.[7]

Powell attempted a survey of students who had left Harvard College for emotional reasons and who had subsequently returned either to be graduated or to leave college again. He secured fairly complete records on forty-nine students, of whom twenty-eight completed their courses and twenty-one were unsuccessful. He examined forty-nine variables in all; in ten of these there were significant differences between the successful and the unsuccessful. Positive variables related to success were:

1) Coming from urban areas rather than rural areas or small towns.
2) Attendance at public rather than private schools.
3) High average grades before leaving.
4) A job while away which required skillful organization of time.
5) One employer rather than two or more during absence.
6) Staying out a year or longer.

7) Rorschach findings suggesting openness or productivity of the individual.

8) Younger than average as compared to older than average students.

Negative variables included:

1) Intellectual ability (whether measured by precollege academic record, college board scores, predicted rank list or scores on special high level intelligence tests).

2) Psychiatric diagnosis.

3) Age at admission.

4) Time of leaving college (whether first or some other year).[8]

Obviously, these findings are based on too few persons to permit generalization, but they are so compatible with intuitive and clinical judgments that larger samples should be studied similarly on many different types of students.

Levenson[9] and his colleagues have been engaged in a study of college students who have withdrawn for psychiatric reasons. Most of them came from colleges in the northeastern part of the United States. In a series of eighty-nine students, he found the following characteristics with great frequency: academic underachievement over a considerable period, low study ability, low social competence, inability to develop and maintain good relations with peers, overestimation of ability followed by discouragement at early lack of success. Many of them had character disorders, with a strong tendency to "act out" their feelings. Family pathology was frequent; gross emotional disturbances were common. One-third came from broken homes, and another third had been subject to intermittent separation of parents. There was a history of interrupted education in 68 per cent of the fathers, 61 per cent of the mothers, and 66 per cent of the siblings. The parents had frequently been actively rebellious. The students experienced strong pressures from their parents to perform well but obtained little effective help from them. As children, they were often perceived by their parents as extensions of themselves. Insight into their problems was slight and they were often surprised that anything had gone wrong with their work; they had no real sense of the meaning of their behavior. Many of them had high ability, though with reduced (often temporarily) capacity to make use of it. Out of forty-six who were treated, twenty-eight had returned to college after being under treatment for periods ranging from two months to one and one-half years. Two of them have subsequently dropped out of college. Several have made satisfactory adjustments in other than academic pursuits.

Knoell has reviewed the research concerning "retention and withdrawal" and concludes pessimistically, "The bulk of the research is unimaginative and unproductive, in terms of discovering new knowledge or attempting to develop techniques for controlling the situation." She criticizes most studies now extant because the topic has been so unlimited that conclusions drawn have little relevance for a particular situation. Academic standards for dismissal and probation have received little attention. Voluntary withdrawals have usually not been separated from dismissals. Little attention has been given to retention and withdrawal in professional education.

Among the questions about which research is needed Knoell lists:

1) Can a college "afford" to admit students who appear quite unlikely to attend for more than a year or two?
2) Is it "healthy" to insist that some students must fail in order to keep the others alert?
3) Should the first semester in college be looked upon as a proving ground to see if students should be in college at all, or should it be viewed as a time of difficult adjustment following which most students will do good work?
4) Should students do all the adjusting or should colleges be willing to review their own procedures continually?
5) What is a reasonable retention rate for most colleges?

She also believes that a classification system for withdrawals should be developed and widely accepted. Her own preference is outlined. Techniques for identifying potential withdrawals are also much needed, together with testing of various methods of reducing the rate among those so designated.[10]

In our culture, we tend to believe that everyone should complete college in the four years succeeding secondary school. Those who do not are considered as dropouts. With the great weight of evidence from studies such as Iffert,[3] Ford and Urban,[6] and Pervin,[5] who find that students return in great numbers to college later on in their lives, it may be that we will have to redefine our own notion of education to conform to what may be a natural rhythm of many normal young people. Some are simply not ready or for some reason not able to complete their college work in the four years after finishing secondary school. To label them dropouts seems to be harsh value judgment (or at least sounds that way) when we may simply be observing a normal process of maturation.

Concentration on a single form of behavior (dropping out of college) which is the end result of many different complex situations may oversimplify the issues involved. To focus all our attention on this phenomenon as if it were a separate entity would be similar to the decision by a physician to treat vomiting as a disease rather than as a symptom of many different kinds of disorders, each with several possible causes. Students may leave college because of lack of finances, illness or injury (their own or relatives'), a change of career choice, academic failure, conduct unacceptable to the college, or for many other reasons. Some causes for withdrawal stem from conditions within the individual, some from college conditions, but more often a combination of inner and outer influences may be delineated.

Oliver Wendell Holmes, the poet, attended the Harvard Law School for a year before transferring to the Medical School. He did so for the best of all possible reasons—"I did not like the one and I did like the other."[11] It is of interest to any college psychiatrist that the elder Holmes practically forced the younger one, the famous jurist, to go to law school.[12] Many years later, in 1886, the younger Holmes gently chided his father before a meeting of the Harvard Law School Association for abandoning law for medicine: "Perhaps, without revealing family secrets, I may whisper that next Monday's poet (at the two hundred and fiftieth anniversary of Harvard) also tasted our masculine diet before seeking more easily digested, if no more nutritious, food elsewhere."[13]

A concerted attack on the problem of attrition should ideally have many aspects, with practically every division or department of the college having a part to play. Among the possible moves that could theoretically reduce the dropout rate would be careful selection of students (not possible for all colleges), effective orientation programs early in the course, good counseling, adequate health services with strong emphasis on prevention of disability, provision of an adequate number of scholarship and loan funds, clearcut and widely understood policies regarding discipline, constant attention to methods of improving teaching, the encouragement of stimulating and satisfying relations between students and faculty, and the development of communication that would permit students to know what is expected of them and faculty members to know what students are thinking. Underlying all these moves would be the attempt to develop a college atmosphere with maximum freedom for the individual, opportunities for both stimulation and privacy, and a relation of the college experience to the salient issues of society and the needs of the student.

The contributions that can be made by a college psychiatric service to lessening the rate of withdrawal of students obviously involves efforts to recognize those students who are unable to cope successfully with their quandaries and to mobilize efforts designed to aid them in dealing with such stresses, while at the same time attempting to minimize those forms of stress that do not contribute to their educational advancement.

Certain background situations occur so often in the histories of those students who seek psychiatric help in the resolution of their quandaries that they can almost be predicted by the experienced psychiatrist. These factors increasing vulnerability to stress include:

Parental conflict or discord, particularly if disagreeing parents try to involve the children in their disputes. Divorce is no more traumatic than a constant state of tension ("cold war," some students call it) between the parents.

Marked contrasts in values between the home environment and those of the college, whether these concern religion, politics, unfair discrimination, or social customs.

Inadequate or improper role models. If the parents or other significant older persons in a child's life show little respect or enthusiasm for intellectual pursuits, he has little reason to do so.

Extreme permissiveness or rigidity or inconsistencies in discipline. Without consistent discipline, a child does not know what to expect and can learn little from experience. As one preparatory school boy said to his psychiatrist, "My parents never tell me what to do. They never stop me from doing anything. I don't have freedom like the other boys have."

Inadequate or improper sexual education. Neither parents, teachers, nor members of the clergy have as yet been able to formulate any program of sexual education that is widely accepted. Both knowledge of and attitudes toward sexual matters are woefully inadequate or inappropriate in many of our young people.

Failure of parents to perceive children as separate individuals. Such parents think of their children as extensions of themselves. They bask in the reflected glory of their children's accomplishments, expect much, but give little real help. The children have gone to college for other peoples' reasons, not their own.

Lack of meaning or purpose in what they have been doing. Their rebellion, desirable though it may be, is not always against any definite limits or standards, because all too often they have discerned none of a rigorous nature.

Poor study habits. Not having been required to work up to, or near, capacity, a very bright youngster who has never developed good work habits finds them very hard to acquire after years of disorganized application.

These sources of increased vulnerability are extensively considered in various chapters in this book and need not be further discussed here. It is desirable, however, that they be known by all educators and that efforts be made to help students in overcoming the effects of such handicaps. If young people who suffered from these conditions were our least capable ones, their significance would be altered. In fact, those who suffer from such handicaps are often among the most gifted of our students; learning to overcome those handicaps may be their most significant educational experiences.

It is unfortunate that the term "dropout" has achieved such wide acceptance. It tends to oversimplify a very complex situation and bring about conclusions that are not justified. For example, some may say that all dropouts are failures, others that the custom is always a good thing and should be encouraged by the colleges. The natural parental attitude when a son or daughter leaves college before graduation is one of regret. Attending college is expensive, an occasion for sacrifice on the part of most parents, and leaving college amounts to an apparent waste of money. Many students who leave college impulsively expect their parents to continue supporting them while they make trips abroad or otherwise try out new experiences while trying to decide what they really want to do. Naturally, this idea is usually looked upon with disfavor by parents, and in many instances rightly so.

When college officials make no efforts to dissuade students from leaving, but instead discuss with them their reasons for doing so and the alternatives of each proposed course of action being considered, parents may feel aggrieved that the college "does not take a stand." Their frustration becomes greater when they "lay the law down" to their offspring or offer them added inducements to stay (which looks like bribery to the student) and find that their influence on them is nil. From that point, it becomes easy to believe that the college encourages students to drop out (and indeed in occasional instances it may). In general, however, the colleges have the same interest as the parents in encouraging students to finish their courses in four consecutive years, but they place an even higher priority on aiding their students to be as well motivated as possible for future constructive development when they are graduated.

In fact, it does little good to try to prevent a student from leaving college when he is convinced that he is wasting his time. For those whom he casts in the role of authority to try to persuade him to stay only serves to convince him that they do not understand him, strengthening his conviction that the college is vastly overrated and has little to offer him in any case. If his college counselors should urge him to leave, this too would be used as evidence that they did not appreciate his true situation and moreover did not want him. A reasonable attitude for a counselor to take might be expressed in these words: "Let's look at the reasons

why you want to drop out now. When this is done you should
decide to go or stay depending on what you think will be best
for you in the long run. In the meantime, we might consider
some of the problems your decision will raise." Such questions as
eligibility for return, appropriate time to apply for readmission
if he can come back, conditions likely to be encountered should
all be discussed until the student has accurate information on
which to base his decision.

There is no reason why the achievement of a low dropout
rate should be sought for its own sake. The college experience
is not a Procrustean bed into which each student should be fitted
regardless of his particular characteristics and needs. A psychosocial moratorium has been found to be of inestimable value in
the development of many persons. When there is reason to
believe that a period of time out of the regular college routine
may be constructive, college officials as well as parents should
adopt the hopeful view. The college is made for students, not
students for the college. Whatever variations appear to be
conducive to a student's ultimate best interests should be seriously considered; when one of them is chosen the student should be
supported or encouraged and not made to feel that he is a
failure. Some students simply cannot achieve maturity in the
college milieu without a period for taking stock of themselves.

Many students consider leaving but finally decide to stay and,
having considered the alternatives, are able to work more effectively than before. For example, a junior in a college with only
a rudimentary counseling service called his father in November
to tell him that he was fed up, getting nowhere, and wasting
money, and that he wished to leave college. After several minutes
of discussion in which the father asked numerous questions with
no implication of judging his decision, he told his son that if he
felt strongly about the matter he thought he should act as he
desired, and that if he needed any help in getting started in his
proposed alternative course it would be available.

The young man decided to stay and was graduated on
schedule. A few years later he was asked how he made his
decision. He said, "What can you do with a father like that? I
called him up, feeling sure that he would give me a big argument.

I was determined to go and prove that I could do something on my own. When he acted so reasonably there was nothing for me to prove by leaving. So I decided to stay."

The criticisms made by those who drop out of school or college are sometimes taken too seriously, i.e., their comments regarding their schools' lack of efficiency are taken to be true. Quite often they are, but even more frequently they are caricatures, more related to the young person's own internal conflicts than to the characteristics of the college itself. Even the person who drops out of school and later returns to finish his academic course seldom agrees with his own former firmly-held opinions.

Whenever the student is so impelled by his conflicts as to be unable to exercise his will power, is lacking in interest or motivation, and is unable to control his impulses toward defeating his own efforts, a period of time out is probably necessary and may be the only constructive course available.

A comparatively minor deviation from normal development in some persons may set in motion a chain reaction leading to profound illness. In others, emotional conflict, even to the extent of serious illness, may stimulate the individuals concerned to creative and satisfying accomplishment, which in turn helps the persons cope successfully with the effects of their illnesses.

In brief, the loss to higher education of so many promising students is a serious drain, harmful to society and the individual alike. Dropping out may be a constructive move for many students, but it is regrettable for many more. The more selective a college is in its admissions policies the higher the percentage of emotional handicaps among those who withdraw. The causes are numerous and diverse. Any program designed to reduce the attrition rate should include various measures to help individual students who are in trouble and should be characterized by constant alertness to the effect of college policies and environmental conditions on the students.

REFERENCES

1. SUMMERSKILL, J.: Dropouts from college. In: *The American College*, N. Sanford, Ed. New York, Wiley, 1962, pp. 627-657.

2. McNEELY, J. H.: *College Student Mortality*. Washington, U. S. Department of Interior Bulletin, Nov. 11, 1937.
3. IFFERT, R. E.: *Retention and Withdrawal of College Students*. Washington, U. S. Department of Health, Education and Welfare, Bulletin No. 1, 1958.
4. SUMMERSKILL, J.: *Op. cit.*, p. 631.
5. PERVIN, L. A.: The later academic, vocational, and personal success of talented dropouts. In: *The College Dropout and Utilization of Talent*, L. A. Pervin, L. E. Reik, and W. Dalrymple, Eds. Princeton, Princeton Univ. Press (To be published in 1966).
6. FORD, D. H., AND URBAN, H. B.: College dropouts: Successes or failures? In: *The College Dropout and Utilization of Talent*, L. A. Pervin, L. E. Reik, and W. Dalrymple, Eds. Princeton, Princeton Univ. Press (To be published in 1966).
7. PESZKE, M. A., AND ARNSTEIN, R. L.: Readmission to College After Psychiatric Medical Leave, In: *The College Dropout and Utilization of Talent*, L. A. Pervin, L. E. Reik, and W. Dalrymple, Eds. Princeton, Princeton Univ. Press (To be published in 1966).
8. POWELL, D. H.: The return of the dropout. *J. Amer. Coll. Health Ass., 13*:475-483, 1965.
9. LEVINSON, E., AND KOHN, M.: A demonstration clinic for college dropouts. *J. Amer. Coll. Health Ass., 12*:382-391, 1964.
10. KNOELL, D. M.: Institutional Research on Retention and Withdrawal. In: *Research on College Students*, H. T. Sprague, Ed. Western Interstate Commission for Higher Education, Boulder, Colorado, and Center for Higher Education, Berkeley, California, pp. 41-65.
11. HOWE, M. A. DEW.: *Holmes of the Breakfast Table*. New York, Oxford, 1939, p. 21.
12. ————: *The Shaping Years*. Cambridge, Harvard, 1957, p. 176.
13. *Ibid.* p. 21.

CHAPTER VII

DRUGS–THEIR USE AND ABUSE BY
COLLEGE STUDENTS

F EW PROBLEMS ARE as vexing to college administrators and
physicians as is the indiscriminate use of drugs by students. In
general, those who become involved in such practices have
emotional difficulties, are dissatisfied with certain aspects of
their own current situation, and are incapable or unwilling to use
more scientific and less hazardous methods of dealing with their
conflicts. Only a minority of troubled people become unwise
users of drugs. Whether an individual resorts to drugs depends
on numerous factors, some of them accidental or fortuitous.
Urban institutions attract people who benefit from the drug
traffic and have an economic interest in encouraging drug use.
Therefore, control of drugs in a college community must include
efforts to close sources of supply as well as to maintain counseling programs designed to aid students in finding appropriate
solutions to their problems.

Concern with unwarranted use of drugs should not obscure
the many benefits that result from their legitimate use. Without
the narcotics, sedatives, tranquilizers, and stimulants there would
be much needless suffering. Mature judgment, heightened by
technical skill, is required in the correct use of these compounds.
In our society, physicians are entrusted with responsibility for
their proper use. When the judgment of the physician is replaced by the whim of the patient, the abuse of drugs becomes
probable. When drugs are used by those with no knowledge of
their limitations and hazards, the possibilities of trouble are
endless.

Information from many sources indicate that the improper use of drugs is increasing. In addition to efforts to achieve their wider use by those who profit from their illegal sale to consumers, some people encourage their use as a means of obtaining intense sensations not otherwise possible. The drug problem is long-standing and ubiquitous, although the particular substances employed vary according to time, place, fashion, and availability.

The purpose of this chapter is to discuss the basic facts about common drugs and the psychological elements involved in their misuse. For a more detailed study of the pharmacology of any particular drug, a standard textbook should be consulted.

Addiction is the most serious result of prolonged use of a drug. It is a condition of mind or body which requires continued use of the drug which caused the addiction if serious physical or mental derangement is to be avoided. True addiction involves habituation, tolerance, and dependence.

Habituation refers to that condition in which one becomes accustomed to, but not seriously dependent upon, a drug. Habituation is an adaptation to the repetitious use of a drug. Alcohol, barbiturates, tobacco, and caffeine ordinarily produce habituation although the first two produce addiction when used excessively. With these drugs, the psychic dependence can usually be relatively easily terminated. The basic phenomenon in habituation or emotional dependence is the development of a sense of well-being after use of a drug. Anxieties and tensions are temporarily relieved. There is little or no tendency to increase the dose. There is some degree of psychological dependence, but no severe physical symptoms when it is withdrawn. As a rule, the detrimental effects are primarily to the individual rather than society.

Tolerance refers to the fact that more and more of a drug must be used to produce effects equivalent to those experienced when first used. Some persons can, however, remain on a constant dose indefinitely without craving more.

Dependence is a disortion of normal physiologic processes which results from prolonged use of addicting drugs so that the presence of an adequate amount of one of these drugs in the body is necessary for the maintenance of psychologic equilibrium.

Dependence is both psychological and physical. Without the drugs, the dependent person becomes sick.

True addiction is produced by opiates and certain synthetic narcotics. It is an overwhelming need to take a drug in increasing doses. The addict uses drugs to forget his problems and quiet his anxieties, and the more often he turns to them for relief, the stronger their hold on him. The effect of addicting drugs is usually detrimental to society as well as to the individual.

Withdrawal of addicting drugs results in characteristic symptoms in the subject, varying with the particular drug involved and the reactivity of the subject. Vomiting, diarrhea, severe abdominal cramps, fever, convulsive seizures, and psychoses are among the various painful and distressing symptoms that result.

Both addicting and habit-forming drugs can be legally obtained only on a physician's prescription. Any other way is illegal and may enmesh a student (or anyone else) in a web of underworld connections that are quite hazardous. Many students are unaware that they are breaking laws by their use of such drugs while others are contemptuous of society's efforts to control drug distribution and use.

NARCOTICS

A narcotic is a drug which causes depression of metabolic activity, mainly of the central nervous system. The term is usually limited in ordinary usage to opium, morphine, heroin, and their derivatives, and to cocaine and marihuana, drugs which are subject to some measure of international control.

Morphine was the first of the narcotics to be isolated from opium. It is highly addictive, but tolerance develops rapidly. Some addicts must use very large doses to keep themselves comfortable.

Heroin, a product of morphine, was at first believed to be a safe substitute for it when it was introduced in 1898, but subsequent study has revealed that it is highly addictive, in fact more so than morphine itself. It is not available by prescription and can be obtained only on the illicit market.

The number of youthful heroin addicts is quite large. Many

of these individuals are initiated into the habit by smoking marihuana cigarettes. When this type of indulgence no longer produces the required stimulation, they then have recourse to more powerful and truly addictive drugs like heroin. Drug "pushers" often persuade marihuana smokers to make the change (there is more profit in heroin), emphasizing the more intensive pleasures obtained from heroin.

Cocaine, a drug derived from the leaves of the cocoa tree in Peru and Bolivia, is a highly addictive drug. At one time, it represented a considerable problem in this country, but at present there are few addicts. It is now seldom used medicinally, although formerly it was used extensivly as a local anesthetic.

Codeine is addictive but much less so than the other narcotics.

There are about 50,000 known addicts in the United States, nearly half of whom are in New York City. However, addiction may occur in any environment or at any social level. Addiction resulting from use of narcotics for severe pain is comparatively infrequent. The critical factor is the personality of the individual who becomes addicted. Many addicts have been excessive users of alcohol; the same characteristics which lead to too much drinking also may be responsible for the use of narcotic drugs.

MARIHUANA

Marihuana comes from the dried flowering tops of a hemp plant, *Cannabis sativa*. Other names for it inclued *hashish, bhang,* and *"mariguana,"* meaning intoxicant. As a narcotic, it has no medicinal use but is employed for its pleasurable psychic effects. It may be smoked (in cigarettes called "reefers"), chewed, ingested, or sniffed. It acts mainly on the central nervous system in a complex way, not yet well understood. When smoked, its effects are felt in a few minutes and usually last from three to five hours, although it is not uncommon for them to persist up to twelve hours. Neither lasting ill effects nor fatalities from acute use have been recorded. The drug causes a combination of excitation and depression. There may be an increase in the pulse rate, a slight rise in blood pressure, some redness of the eyes, and a minimal increase in blood sugar and in the basal metabolic rate. An increase in appetite, especially for sweets, may occur, as may dryness of mouth and throat.

Psychologically it produces a dreamy state of altered consciousness; disconnected ideas come rapidly, and seem uncontrollable. There are often feelings of extreme well-being, exaltation, and excitement, a condition referred to as being "high." At other times the subject may experience a "down" with moodiness, fear of death, and panic. Ideas may occur in disrupted sequence with memory varying from being very acute to quite unreliable. Seconds may seem like minutes, minutes may seem like hours. Distance and sound may be magnified. Space may seem "expanded," the head may feel swollen and the extremities heavy. Pleasant visual hallucinations with sexual content sometimes occur. Behavior may be impulsive when the mood is elevated. Random ideas are soon expressed in speech. The individual may experience sensations of floating, ringing in the ears, and tremors. Persons taking the drug may be quiet and drowsy when alone though restless, talkative, laughing, or joking when in company.

Artists and musicians sometimes claim an increase in their ability to appreciate their own work or that of their colleagues.

Large doses may produce confusion, disorientation, and increased anxiety. Psychoses may develop, lasting hours or sometimes weeks.

Marihuana smoking does not produce a tolerance for the drug, nor is there a true addiction with withdrawal symptoms. Those familiar with the drug and its users believe that it may lead to experimenting with stronger drugs such as heroin, not because of its chemical effects but because of the personal associations formed by people who use marihuana. Smoking is usually done in groups, many members of which have motives somewhat less than idealistic. Those who use the drug usually do so in order to get a feeling of contentment, inner satisfaction, intimacy, and to enjoy the free play of their imagination. If these sensations are not realized, it is quite understandable that they would look to another drug for these effects. Little by little the capacity to free one's self from such experimentation becomes impaired, and what began as an experiment becomes a powerful habit.

Goodman and Gilman state that the typical marihuana user

is usually twenty to thirty years old; he is idle, lacking in initiative, usually frustrated, often sexually maladjusted (homosexual), and seeks distraction or escape through a bogus conviviality. He almost always has major personality defects, is impulsive or otherwise emotionally unstable.[1] In colleges, the use of marihuana may be a kind of conventional way of provoking disapproval or retaliation from society, and hence it constitutes an open method of rebellion. Once the stupidity and futility of such behavior becomes evident, most students give it up, unless their personality problems continue to be so severe that they are unable or unwilling to seek out more satisfactory methods of dealing with them.

SEDATIVES AND HYPNOTICS

A sedative is a drug which depresses the central nervous system, especially at its higher levels, and thus decreases nervousness, anxiety, fear, or excitement—but not usually to the point of producing sleep. A hypnotic is a drug used to induce sleep. It depresses the central nervous system more profoundly than does a sedative but the duration of its effect is shorter.

Barbiturates are hypnotics; there are more than 2500 different varieties. At least fifty of these have been marketed. Some are short-acting and others longer-acting. Slang names for them include "goof balls," "red birds," and "yellow jackets." The extent of their action ranges from very slight depression to death from paralysis of the respiratory center. Dangers associated with their use include both acute poisoning and addiction by chronic usage.

Barbiturates are not only habit forming but they cause addiction when taken in large and uncontrolled amounts. Sudden withdrawal after continued usage may produce severe symptoms or even fatalities. Many people use them as intoxicants instead of alcohol. More deaths are caused by overdoses of barbiturates, taken either accidentally or as a means of suicide, than by any other poison except carbon monoxide. They are not only harmful to individuals but present a serious social problem.[2]

Chloral hydrate was a very popular drug many years ago and dropped from favor as the barbiturates became more popular.

But they have been used to such excess, often with harmful effects, that they have become suspect, and chloral hydrate has returned to favor as a useful sedative. However, like other hypnotic drugs, it may also cause addiction when used in an uncontrolled manner.

The current production of sedative and hypnotic drugs exceeds legitimate medical need by a considerable margin. This alone suggests that many of them are being used improperly. The Food and Drug Administration has estimated that at least one-half the annual production of stimulant and depressant pills is being diverted into illicit channels.

PSYCHIC ENERGIZERS

Amphetamines (benzedrine and dexedrine) belong to a group of drugs called psychic energizers which act mainly on those parts of the brain concerned with the elevation of mood. They are often used in the treatment of patients suffering from depression.

In small dosages, these drugs postpone fatigue, prevent sleepiness, promote alertness, and increase initiative, though they have little effect on intellectual capacity. In larger doses they can produce tremors, restlessness, increased activity to the point of agitation, and insomnia. Judgment becomes impaired. Tragic highway accidents have been caused by sleepy drivers who use them in order to stay awake. As the dosage becomes larger they may bring on headache, dizziness, palpitation, apprehension, delirium, extreme depression and fatigue, convulsions, and finally coma and death. In fatal cases, brain hemorrhages are often found; these result from a strong constricting action on blood vessels which leads to their rupture.

Among illegal users of the amphetamines the drugs are known as "Bennies" or "pep pills."

True addiction is not common but psychological habituation often occurs. Addicts may manifest (in addition to the symptoms already mentioned) combativeness and psychoses marked by auditory and hallucinations, often accompanied by paranoid delusions.

Many students take an amphetamine with the assumption that it will help them think more clearly. Smith and Beecher have shown that amphetamines impair rather than improve judgment. They asked seventy-eight students to solve twenty-five calculus problems and then estimate the number of correct solutions. This was done on five occasions, sometimes using an amphetamine, sometimes a sedative, and at other times a placebo. Those who had been given an amphetamine showed the poorest judgment.[3] Because of the small amount of change the authors stress the need for cautious generalization.

Caffeine is a relatively harmless drug. It occurs naturally in coffee, tea, and cocoa; it can also be made synthetically. In ordinary dosage (1 to 2 cups of coffee) it increases the speed of mental functioning, raises the spirits, produces more acute and discriminating sensations, facilitates the association of ideas, and occasionally in some persons produces insomnia. It is an ingredient of numerous headache remedies because it reduces pain by decreasing the distention of arterial blood vessels. Small doses may improve mental and muscular performance but larger doses impair them. Although ideas become clearer, thought flows more easily and rapidly, and fatigue and drowsiness disappear, connected thought may be made more difficult, since impressions follow one another so rapidly that attention is distracted.[4] For this reason, students should be strongly advised to avoid those pills containing caffeine so often promoted around colleges and universities during examination periods. Caffeine dosages beyond those occurring in coffee, tea, and cola drinks are neither necessary nor desirable for the best use of one's mental facilities.

During periods of acute stress, such as approaching examinations, students may have used stimulants or sedatives unwisely and become anxious or fatigued. They then often try to counteract the effects of one class of drugs by the use of another. This practice is dangerous and should always be discouraged.

Psychic energizers are not desirable as a remedy for sleepiness or fatigue because of the danger of habit formation and because they remove necessary warning signals of overwork or overstrain. They have several legitimate medical uses, but should never be taken except under competent medical direction and supervision.

TRANQUILIZERS

In 1952, a new class of drugs was introduced into medical

practice. Popularly known as tranquilizers, these drugs promote a sense of calmness in an individual without impairing his ability to recognize the nature or significance of events occurring around him. They have been influential in decreasing the disturbing and dangerous behavior of acutely ill mental patients, thus permitting shortened hospitalization for psychiatric disorders or treatment without hospitalization. Those patients who respond well to such drugs may develop an attitude of indifference both to their symptoms and their surroundings, although they remain quite aware of what is going on around them.

The number of tranquilizing drugs is already great and increasing constantly, but relatively few of them are widely used. Some of them are particularly suited for treating destructive and aggressive patients, others for those who are depressed and retarded, and still others for anxiety and tension states and for the promotion of muscle relaxation. Many of them increase the action of any sedatives or narcotics that may be in the body at the same time.

Although they are relatively safe in proper dosage, they may produce "side reactions" including drowsiness, a variety of unpleasant physical symptoms, jaundice, lowered blood pressure, and allergic reactions. In some instances, they may inhibit the production of white blood cells. This can be a very serious matter. Obviously they should never be taken without competent medical supervision if fatalities are to be avoided.

After prolonged use, some tranquilizers create a physical dependence. Upon withdrawal, the patient may suffer from increased irritability of the nervous system or even convulsions. Such reactions indicate a true addiction.

As might be expected, students and others who have become multihabituated to other drugs may try tranquilizers in the hope that they will produce new sensations or elaborations of the older ones.

ALCOHOL

Alcohol is widely used in nearly all countries, sometimes for social reasons, at other times for personal ones. In the United States, probably two-thirds of the people drink alcoholic beverages at some time, usually in social situations. Many persons, the number unknown, use alcohol regularly with no apparent ill effects. A small number, possibly five to six million persons, use it excessively and cause suffering of varying degree to themselves or others. Members of this group may be called "alcoholics." They exhibit the long-term effects of a combination of psychological problems and also the unwise use of alcohol in an attempt to alleviate them.

Alcoholism is defined by Chafetz and Demone[5] as a chronic behavioral disorder manifested by undue preoccupation with drinking to the detriment of physical and mental health, by a loss of control, and by a self-destructive attitude in dealing with personal relationships and life situations.

Although the number of alcoholic men is much greater than alcoholic women, the number of the latter is on the increase. It is more difficult to recognize female than male alcoholics because of various social conventions which serve to protect them.

Most of those who are heavy drinkers in college revert afterwards to social drinking. However, about 3 to 4 per cent go on to develop chronic alcoholism. The progression from heavy drinking to addiction takes about fifteen years.

No single factor can be cited as the cause of alcoholism. Most persons who suffer from this disorder have intermittent strong feelings or dissatisfaction in their relations with others. One patient expressed his predicament eloquently when he said, "It takes about two Manhattans to make me feel normal." A feeling of social inferiority is common. Depression is frequent.

Young alcoholics have a very poor prognosis. Morning and solitary drinking are ominous signs. Alcoholics have a reputation of being very untruthful because of their ready use of denial as a means of dealing with their problems. They mean to tell the truth about their behavior, and even hope that they do, but still they consistently misrepresent the extent of their actions whenever alcohol is concerned.

Learning how to use alcohol without getting into trouble is an important task in college. Those who are brought up as abstainers may adhere to this code if no serious psychological problems intervene. Banning alcohol is no solution, as the failure of the prohibition amendment demonstrated. For relief of temporary tensions, alcohol may be less dangerous than many other agents. A good rule to observe is that if one needs alcohol he should not use it. Everyone should observe occasional periods of complete abstinence to see how dependent he is on alcohol. Those who use alcohol socially, and successfully, have learned how to "stretch it out" by appropriate dilution and recognition of the point at which physiological effects become prominent, thus avoiding the unpleasant and destructive effects.

College administrators are in a very difficult situation, particularly in the public colleges and universities and in those with church affiliations. Most of them learn the varying degrees of tolerance toward the use of alcohol shown by persons influential in the institution and thus achieve an uneasy truce among all those persons with strong but contradictory ideas of what policies they should pursue. The most destructive of all situations is that in which the regulations regarding alcohol are unenforceable and thus teach disrespect for the authority of the college, university, or community. Rules that are not, and cannot, be enforced are worse than none at all.

TOBACCO

Tobacco smoking is an example of a drug used for the achievement of pleasurable sensations, but which differs from others (except alcohol) in that it is socially approved or tolerated on a large scale. Although many persons who are dependent upon tobacco do not think of themselves as being addicted to a drug, some of them are in fact perilously close to this state. The distress of those who smoke heavily and attempt to stop is quite acute and involves both physiological and psychological discomfort. Unfortunately, the damage done by excessive cigarette smoking is manifested only after long usage. Since it does not occur in all heavy smokers, and takes the form of chronic bronchitis, cancer of the lung, or emphysema (diseases which have other causes as well) many people are lulled into a feeling of false security. Heart disease is also more common in heavy smokers; their life expectancy is several years less than that of non-smokers. Those who have a vested interest in the tobacco industry maintain that the evidence of harm from smoking is inconclusive, but the consensus seems to be against them. The fact that millions of persons persist in smoking in spite of the known hazards may be taken as one of the proofs for the presence of addiction.*

PSYCHOTOMIMETICS

Drugs which produce mental states resembling those of persons suffering from psychoses are known as psychotomimetic drugs. When these were first introduced into medicine it was hoped that it would be possible, by studying their effects, to determine the causes of psychoses which stem from unknown agents or seemingly from emotional causes. Knowledge derived from such experimentation might be applied to the treatment of mental illness whose causes had been previously obscure. Numerous research workers have been encouraged by their results in working with severely disturbed persons, particularly those suffering from alcoholism. However, their work has been seriously complicated by the unscientific use of these drugs by persons who are not aware of the hazards involved or who willfully disregard them. At present there are no indications for the use of such drugs except by responsible research workers who are trying to unravel the obscurities of mental disorder.

Those drugs in the psychotomimetic group which produce hallucinations are called the hallucinogenic drugs. These drugs produce a transitory psychotic state with considerable resemblance to schizophrenia. They are mainly depressing in their effects and cause lassitude, muscle relaxation, lowered blood pressure, slow respiration, diminished heart action, decreased reaction time, and, if the dose is large enough, delirium.

One of the most common of these drugs is Lysergic acid diethylamide or LSD. It was discovered in 1943 by a Swiss scientist, A. Hofmann, who was preparing this organic compound when he noticed sensations of dizziness, restlessness, and disorientation toward his environment. He subsequently took some of this drug and found that it was indeed the cause of his

----

* Only a few persons would agree that tobacco is truly addictive; I think that the symptoms exhibited by heavy smokers trying to quit justifies the use of the term.

symptoms, which included, among other things, fantastic and colorful visions. Like others, this drug produces a variety of symptoms in addition to the psychological disturbances. These include fever, dilation of the pupils, lowering of the blood pressure, slowing of the pulse, and slight shortness of breath, as well as skin sensations from pilomotor stimulation, all symptoms resulting from stimulation of the sympathetic nervous system. Pharmacologists believe that tolerance soon develops, but our experience indicates that for some persons the same effects may be induced by lesser amounts when they are used repeatedly.

Peyote (or mescaline) is obtained from a cactus plant which grows in the Rio Grande valley in southwestern United States. Peyote buttons are the tops of cactus plants which have been cut off and dried. They contain mescaline, a poisonous alkaloid. The buttons are used by Indians in religious ceremonies.

Mescaline produces visual hallucinations of various types. They may consist of brightly colored geometric figures, animals, or people. Color and space perception is impaired. Some of the perceptual changes are similar to those produced by LSD. Mescaline does not cause addiction. Extreme anxiety states may be produced in schizophrenic patients and in some persons even small doses may cause a disturbance in thinking similar to schizophrenia.

During the early years of experimentation with LSD and other hallucinogenic drugs, the adverse effects were not considered to be very serious. In recent years, however, numerous cases of prolonged adverse reactions have been reported especially with LSD, lasting from a few months up to two years. Some of these cases undoubtedly represent psychotic decompensations; others are depressive reactions, paranoid reactions, and release of pre-existing psychopathic or asocial trends. Severe agitated depressions with anxiety, guilt, hypochondriasis, and shame have lasted as long as eight months after a single dose of LSD. Schizophrenic reactions have occurred in a number of persons who may have had pre-schizophrenic tendencies. Subjects who have taken the drug several times may develop hallucinosis lasting as long as six months or more after the last exposure to the drug.[6] Both pleasant and frightening effects are noted. The frightening hallucinations tend to be involuntary and may consist of visions of cats, crabs, insects, corpses, or the skulls of familiar people. The pleasant sensations are apt to be semi-voluntary, since the subject can make them appear and disappear at will. Most of these consist of shimmering lights or droplets of color. These hallucinations are not characteristic of schizophrenia but are characteristic of the effect of this drug. Patients have insight even when they know that they are hallucinating. It is possible that there may be a specific toxic effect of these drugs on the retina, optic pathways, or visual cortex.

Many of the subjects who take hallucinogenic drugs do so more or less indiscriminately, sometimes using one drug and sometimes another. This custom has been called "multihabituation" by Cohen and Ditman.[7] As the use of these drugs increases in frequency, it is probable that there will be more and more instances of hallucinosis of the type described here.

Among those who become enamoured of taking hallucinogens, there is a constant search for new drugs. Such bizarre agents as morning glory seeds (some varieties of which are contaminated with an hallucinogenic substance), powdered nutmeg, and concentrated tincture of belladonna are occasionally used by the heedless, in spite of the fact that these agents not only make them ill but may also result in their death. Adolescents have used airplane model glue for "glue-sniffing" parties, sometimes with consequent destruction of brain cells resulting in permanent mental retardation. Ether "sniffers" have been known for many years as a troubled and unstable group.

Ludwig and Levine interviewed twenty-seven patients extensively at the U. S. Public Health Service Hospital in Lexington, Kentucky, twenty-four males and three females, who were post-narcotic drug addict inpatients, all of whom had used hallucinogenic drugs repeatedly.[8]

The substances they had used included peyote, mescaline (a derivative of peyote), LSD, psilocybin, various combinations of these drugs, and also one or more of these drugs with opium, marihuana, or the amphetamines added to them.

These patients said that they could use the hallucinogenic agents interchangeably, and that their effects were so similar that they could not tell one from the other.

Whereas the narcotic drugs, the barbiturates, and the

amphetamines are always available for a price, the hallucinogens appear only sporadically because the demand for these drugs is not constant. Since there is no physical addiction and no withdrawal symptoms, the possibility of great financial gain is much less than in the sale of narcotics. Many fewer people use these drugs than use barbiturates or amphetamines. Most of them are not available by prescription and few physicians use them. Peyote is the drug most often accessible and the most plentiful. Mescaline, LSD, and psilocybin are much less frequently obtainable. These drugs are more easily obtained in the larger cities than anywhere else, particularly New York and Boston. On the West Coast, Los Angeles, San Francisco, and San Diego are the main centers of distribution.

The hallucinogenic drugs are frequently used in social situations where friends tend to share the drugs, wheras this custom is rare with the narcotics. They are frequently dispensed at parties. Hallucinogens are sold by individuals who also deal in barbiturates, amphetamines, and marihuana. The "pushers" of narcotic drugs look down on the "pill addicts." Business dealings among those engaged in the hallucinogenic drug traffic are more apt to be friendly and on a personal basis than purely financial. The source of supply of LSD and psilocybin is unknown. They seem to be available on a sporadic and limited basis.

There appear to be three main patterns of hallucinogenic drug use: (1) those who prefer narcotics but who use the hallucinogenic agents for kicks or for curiosity; (2) the "professional potheads," who have had extensive experience with various drugs but are looking for something new—they see themselves as creative or "arty," as intellectuals who are in some kind of rebellion, often spending long weekends together and seldom taking the drug while alone; (3) the relatively small number of people who take only the hallucinogenic agents, usually over a long period of time—most of these use the drug as a means of attaining some personal goal, e.g., attempting to achieve increased sensitivity or greater insight into themselves.

The use of hallucinogenic drugs does not appear either to stimulate or diminish sexual drive. Those who engage in sexual activities while under the influence of the drugs, however, may find the sensations much more intense than usual. Users agreed that peyote tended to suppress the sexual drive.

Most of the patients claimed that hallucinogenic agents did not produce addiction in a physical sense, and that no withdrawal symptoms were experienced other than an occasional short period of "let-down." They did think that a psychological addiction took place, however. Some of them believed that a person had to have a psychological disorder to become psychologically addicted to the hallucinogens.

Opinions differed as to whether or not tolerance developed. Some thought it did, and others thought it worked in reverse, i.e., that they became more susceptible or sensitive to the effects of the hallucinogens after a time, and could then achieve the same effects on a lower dosage. They frequently said that they could sometimes *almost* slip back into the same frame of mind they had had while taking the drug even without taking it. Several felt that a tolerance did develop to mescaline and peyote. Almost all the patients felt that the hallucinogens were safe from a physical point of view, and that they knew of no one's dying from an over-dose, or of any consistently harmful effects. The dangers seem to be related to the psychological reactions produced by the drugs and the poorer reality testing which seemed in evidence after taking them. For example, a person might feel that he was going insane, or would become frightened and try to get somebody to knock him out. One individual experienced homicidal impulses toward a cab driver. Some patients reported the acting out of homosexual urges. Other persons became psychotic after prolonged use, but they considered this danger to be greater with the amphetamines than with the hallucinogenic drugs. One patient spoke of an individual who tried to stab himself because he believed he was invincible. Another tried to jump off a bridge because he thought his mind and body were separate. Another tried to jump out a window because he believed his body to be weightless. Two patients reported near accidents while driving under the influence of the hallucinogens.

The above observations of Ludwig's and Levin's patients are remarkably consistent with those from many other sources.

Those promoting the general use of these hallucinogens

believe they "expand consciousness" and give a man or woman new insights and new intellectual powers.* Wasson says, speaking of mushroom poison, "It permits you to see, more clearly than our perishing mortal eye can see, vistas beyond the horizons of this life, to travel backwards and forwards in time, to enter other planes of existence, even . . . to know God."[9] Such testimony is common and makes it easy to understand the fascination these drugs exert on many people, especially on those of college age.

Our young people are being told that there is little hazard in the use of hallucinogens[10]—"less harmful than aspirin or alcohol, less dangerous than riding in a motorcar"—and that the spiritual and intellectual rewards are vivid, wonderful, inexpressible. The case is made that men's minds are now "imprisoned" in verbal habits and formalities, and that the drugs offer an escape to a word-free paradise. The claim is advanced that the drugs "free" the mind for creative activity that would otherwise be beyond reach, and that subsequent psychological functioning, after the effects of the drugs have worn off, will be better than before. Sociability is a keynote of the new drug promotion; often the hallucinogens are taken in a house-party group, and the resulting experiences and hallucinations are sympathetically shared. Support for this promotion is beginning to develop in college faculties, in the ranks of the ministry, and even among physicians. It is no wonder that numbers of our young people are beginning to pay attention to the siren song of "consciousness expansion."

On the claim that the hallucinogens "free" the mind for creative work, it must be said that up to now we have had any amount of rhapsodic talk and writing, but no responsible proof. Meanwhile, the evidence accumulates steadily to indicate that the drugs do exert powerful and often damaging effects on the human system. Cole reports that all the psychotomimetic agents can effectively impair behavior, if only through autonomic side effects.[11]

Recent clinical observations of this writer and his associates suggest that people who are attracted to the hallucinogenic drugs

---

* The following few pages are taken from an editorial by the writer originally published in the *Journal of the American Medical Association*, Sept. 12, 1963, and reproduced here by the permission of the editor of the *Journal*.

are often those most likely to be harmed by them. Many who have tried the drugs were persons who had difficulty in dealing with reality, who sought in drugs a quick and easy method of changing reality, and who hoped for a prompt solution to their inner conflicts. Two patients explain:

> Most people take the drugs because they think it will help them solve their problems. They feel it will alter their sense of reality and that they will be able to cope with their new insights. I felt that taking the drug might help straighten me out.
>
> I was mixed up. I couldn't communicate with people and I felt taking the drugs would help . . .

The statements of other patients, and other witnesses, begin to tell us a great deal about the hazards in the use of the drugs:

> I kept a journal while on the drugs. Later I read it and it was horrible. People were tearing each other apart. Also, I felt I was reading the worst pornography I had ever read.
>
> Your mind seems to think about all the things it ordinarily dosen't want to think about.
>
> I had a horror-show after taking the morning-glory seeds. I felt my brain would blow up. I felt I was losing my mind. I felt I was going to die but I couldn't communicate it to anyone. I tried to tell my brother but couldn't make him understand.
>
> (On experiences with LSD-25) I had a compulsive urge to do violence to my children . . . nor do I know myself to this day how great the gap was between the violent thoughts in my mind and their possible execution.[12]
>
> (A research worker who took a number of psychoactive drugs, including tranquillizers, sedatives, alcohol, and LSD-25) Man continues his search for the jinni that will come out of a bottle and do his work for him. I did not find it. Each of the drugs I took, in one way or another, impaired what I conceive to be optimal functioning. None of them gave me any substantial sense of betterment.[13]

For good reason the fraternity jargon of the drug users includes the phrase "hell experience" as well as "heaven experience," although the "hell experience" is ordinarily soft-pedaled in the talk and writing of the drug promoters. In our files is the report of a student who took one of the drugs and spent a whole day living the nightmare that he was only six inches tall; during this period he was psychically helpless and had to be cared for by friends. In another case, two friends took the drug together: one rather enjoyed it; the other sobbed uncontrollably for three hours. Asher[14] reported that as a consequence of a single ingestion of LSD-25 he spent several days in bed, either babbling or crying, or limp and apathetic; for some weeks afterwards he was subject to horrid, involuntary hallucinations, and for some months was dependent on sleeping pills for rest at night. One individual known to the writer has taken LSD-25 several times; he can now hallucinate at will, without resorting to the drug.

Our accumulating day-to-day experience with patients suffering the consequences of the hallucinogens demonstrates beyond question that these drugs have the power to damage the individual psyche, indeed to cripple it for life. In our own experience, several students have had to be hospitalized for long periods following the ingestion of small amounts of drugs. We have as yet no basis for identifying persons for whom the drugs are "safe" and persons whom the drugs will take into a prolonged, perhaps permanent, psychosis. Indeed, the effect of the drugs upon any one individual appears to vary a great deal from one ingestion to the next. We do observe that, whereas rational and prudent individuals have a tendency to stay clear of these drugs, neurotic and unstable people are unduly attracted to them. We have as yet no wholly reliable information as to the long-range effects of taking the hallucinogens over a protracted period of time, but there are already some distressing indications that their habitual use will lead, in some persons at least, to looseness in thinking and difficulty in communicating coherently. Until we know otherwise, it is prudent for us to assume, further, that regular use of the hallucinogens will prepare individuals to "move up" to other and more powerful drugs, such as morphine or heroin.

It is necessary to record that numbers of people promoting the hallucinogens are not aware of, and evidently do not care about, the harm caused by their use. These persons typically pay little attention to precautions that any responsible investigator would demand. They wish to escape from the "medical model" of research, and indeed often urge that the experimenters and the subject undergo the effects of the drug at the same time. "Research" conducted on these terms is, of course, casting a shadow on the work of responsible investigators in psychopharmacology. As Beecher says, "The study of mind-distorting drugs is a very small part of a large and richly rewarding new area of work: quantitative study of the effects of drugs on the mind. Such work is found to have great influence on the development of pharmacology, psychology, and psychiatry, as well as in the care of the sick. It must not be allowed to suffer because of ill-considered activities such as those recently reported in the national press. Aspects of such work concern the sedatives, the 'tranquillizers,' the sleep producers, the pain relievers, the ego-depressants, the anesthetics. Thus, there is a continuum from the slightest mental effects to oblivion."[15]

Schultes describes the symptoms of mushroon (Psilocybe mexicana) intoxication as "a kaleidoscopic play of visual hallucinations in color, muscle relaxation, flaccidity, mydriasis (marked dilatation of the pupils of the eyes), later followed by a period of emotional disturbance such as extreme hilarity and difficulty in concentrating." Lassitude, mental and physical depression, and serious alteration of time and space perception follow. The subject becomes indifferent to his environment; his dream state becomes more important and real to him than the actual surroundings.[16]

Most recently comes Grinker's warning: "Now the deleterious effects are becoming more obvious. Latent psychotics are disintegrating under the influence of even single doses; long-continued LSD experiences are subtly creating a psychopathology. Psychic addiction is being developed, and the lay public is looking for psychiatrists who specialize in its administration."[17]*

Drug use of significant extent by college students is characterized by paradoxes. It is both an individual and a group phenomenon, it represents both rebellion (against the "bourgeois" society and adult authority) and conformity (to contemporary peer "fashion" and in-group dictates). It constitutes a search for

_____

* End of quoted material from *Journal of the American Medical Association,* Sept. 12, 1963.

a panacea to avoid old problems but in reality it brings on new ones although there is the illusion of "freedom."

These drugs inhibit productivity, creativity, and meaningful interpersonal relationships. Ironically, to himself the subject seems improved in all three. (Musicians often claim that they can play faster or with greater originality when they are "high," although there is no evidence that this is true. Under the influence of LSD, subjects claim to know what others are thinking; again, the claim has not been substantiated.)

In terms of college fashion, drugs are "in," and their use has a language associated with it which is employed only by initiates, thus reinforcing their status as belonging to a highly specialized or exclusive group. The vocabulary has sexual connotations; in at least one instance (the phrase "to turn on") it has filtered down to nonspecific colloquial usage.

If drug use represents membership in one group, it also represents a negative reaction against "others," and particularly those thought of as constituting "the Establishment." Certain forms and manifestations of rebellion are characteristic of adolescence and young adulthood, and in fact many contribute significantly to personal growth, social progress, and intellectual accomplishment. Chronic drug use does not foster creativity or constructive action. In general addicts are merely "making do" or substituting bogus experiences for real ones.

The distinction should be made between those who are curious about the effects of drugs, experiment with them, and then abandon them and those who are searching for a panacea. The latter as a group share certain characteristics: feelings of inadequacy, isolation, anonymity, disillusion, and fear of intimacy. Marihuana smoking, perhaps partly because it usually is a group activity, seems to encourage communication and increase intimacy. Occasionally, a person who is depressed can smoke marihuana and at that time re-enter the kind of fantasy or speculative life that he indulged in when not depressed. Some of the people who feel inadequate take drugs because they see in it something new and daring. They can look upon themselves with somewhat more favor for taking the risks involved, especially when they receive approval from their friends. One very sick student, who was bothered by distressing fantasies during his illness, wished to take LSD because he thought it would help him get rid of them. The psychotomimetics produce intense aesthetic, sensory, and psychological experiences—the individual gets "outside himself."

The fringe groups existing around large urban universities constitute a danger because they recruit students into the drug-users' world. College administrators should be aware of their activities and, if possible, institute some sort of prevention.

Researchers have discovered that some so-called "normal" volunteers are in fact a self-selected group of disturbed and inadequate persons. Those who tend to fall into this category are often homosexuals, persons with character disorders who have proclivities toward acting out, or hysterical individuals.

Once vulnerable students start taking drugs their whole lives seem to revolve around them. Since their preoccupation is incompatible with studying, many of them fail in their work.

The greatest danger is not among graduate students but among adolescents from sixteen to twenty who are often full of despair, uncertainty, and anxiety, a mark of their age and of the times. These people are easy prey in high school and early college days. They see the promise of a new land of love and brotherhood, rosy vistas of the future. The drug pushers seem to have a perfect plan for the young and despairing adolescent boy or girl. Many of the urban high schools have problems more serious than those encountered by the colleges. Youngsters may start using the drugs while still in high school, while others are introduced to them in college. The important consideration in the management of the total problem is that control is possible only by cooperation of parents, town and city officials, high school and college administrators, and the special law enforcement officers of the state and federal governments who are concerned with narcotics and other habit-forming drugs.

Taking drugs is one of the ways in which people try to solve their emotional problems while in college. It is an unhealthy way. Colleges must see to it that a better way is provided by helping students deal with their own problems and trying to minimize the unfortunate influences stemming from neighborhood fringe groups. Those who have been taking drugs over a long period of time should not be readmitted to college unless they have been successfully treated and the drug habit cured. They are very disturbed people.

Sons or daughters of physicians are often supplied with sedatives by their parents. Frequently they let their friends have them, too, thus encouraging the idea that their use is harmless. Many believe that there is some drug which can serve as an antidote to any discomfort, emotional or physical, if only it can be found. They change impulsively from one drug to another, trying anything they can find or which may be suggested by their friends.

Vulnerability to emotional disorders is so intense in some students that they use drugs more or less constantly. The great majority, however, use them unwisely only when they are under the temporary stresses of examinations or some kind of bereavement.

College students probably use drugs less than do those outside college who have little motivation and much time on their hands, but their habits and activities are always more newsworthy than those of other young people. The use of drugs is most apt to occur when groups of young people run together, each reinforcing the other in urging experimentation with some new drug. Even in quite "respectable" communities, gangs of boys and girls may range over the whole countryside, trying all sorts of new experiences, doing bizarre things, experimenting sexually, smoking marihuana, taking dexedrine, peyote and mescaline, and LSD and psilocybin when these are available. It is an "in" thing to take drugs, lose one's virginity, and be very tolerant and sophisticated about antisocial attitudes toward manners, dress, and personal grooming. At the same time these youngsters may cultivate a highly moral attitude about important social evils, especially those involving exploitation of some groups by others.

Once an individual becomes so "advanced" in his drug experimentation that he realizes he is just another drug addict, it is a difficult matter for him to retrace his steps. Most young people back off before they have permanently and irrevocably harmed themselves, but some continue their self-defeating conduct and gradually drift into the more bohemian sections of large cities or into mental hospitals and jails.

REFERENCES

1. GOODMAN, L. S., AND GILMAN, A.: *The Pharmacological Basis of Therapeutics,* 2nd Ed. New York, Macmillan, 1955, p. 174.

2. A.M.A. Committee on Alcoholism and Addiction and Council on Mental Health: Dependence on barbiturates and other sedative drugs. *J. Amer. Med. Ass., 193*:673-677, 1965.

3. SMITH, G. M., AND BEECHER, H. K.: Drugs and judgment: effects of amphetamine and secobarbital on self-evaluation. *J. Psychol., 58*:397-405, 1964.

4. GROLLMAN, A.: *Pharmacology and Therapeutics.* Philadelphia, Lea, 1960, p. 214.

5. CHAFETZ, M. E., AND DEMONE, H. W.: *Alcoholism and Society.* New York, Oxford, 1962, p. 4.

6. ROSENTHAL, S. H.: Persistent hallucinosis following repeated administration of hallucinogenic drugs. *Amer. J. Psychiat., 121*:238-244, 1964.

7. COHEN, S., AND DITMAN, K. S.: Prolonged adverse reactions to lysergic acid and diethylamide. *Arch. Gen. Psychiat. (Chicago), 8*:475, 1963.

8. LUDWIG, A. M., AND LEVINE, J.: Patterns of hallucinogenic drug abuse, *J. Amer. Med. Ass., 191*:92-96, 1965.

9. WASSON, B. G.: Mushroom rites in Mexico. *Harvard Rev., 1*:14, 1963.

10. HEARD, G.: Can this drug enlarge man's mind? *Horizon, 5*:115, 1963.

11. COLE, J. O.: Drugs and control of the mind. *In Control of the Mind,* S. M. Farber, and R. H. L. Wilson, Eds. New York, McGraw-Hill, 1961, p. 114.

12. ASHER, H.: They split my personality, *Saturday Review,* June 1963, pp. 42-43.

13. BENNETT, C. C.: Drugs and I. In: *Drugs and Behavior,* L. Uhr, and J. G. Miller, Eds. New York, Wiley, 1960, p. 608.

14. Asher: *Loc cit.*

15. BEECHER, H. K.: Science, drugs, students. *Harvard Alumni Bull., 65*:338, 1963.

16. SCHULTES, R.: Hallucinogenic plants of the new world. *Harvard Rev., 1*:29, 1963.

17. GRINKER, R. R., SR.: Lysergic acid diethylamide. Editorial. *Arch. Gen. Psychiat. (Chicago), 8*:425, 1963.

CHAPTER VIII

STUDENT ROOTLESSNESS AND RESTLESSNESS

A DECADE AGO college students were being criticized because they were apathetic toward public affairs and obsessed with security. Now they are said to be restless, dissatisfied with their college experience and the world as it is, and excessive in their protests against conditions of which they disapprove. It does not oversimplify the situation too much to call the fifties the decade of apathy and the sixties the decade of discontent.

Dissatisfaction with conditions as they exist is almost a hallmark of youth. The college student who accepts conditions in the world as he finds them without question, and who automatically believes all that he is taught, is not a suitable subject for higher education. Discontent, questioning and challenging attitudes, and a desire to reorganize institutions as he finds them are indications that a college student is using his own mind and benefiting from his college experience. But individual rebellion of a constructive nature may at times veer in the direction of group rebellion with at times destructive overtones.

The causes of restlessness and rootlessness are numerous and varied. They are never the same in any two individuals. Some of them are social, some cultural, others the result of individual experiences. They combine in various proportions in individuals or in groups. Some of them may be fanned into grotesque proportions by the local conditions of a single institution or be distorted by publicity which concentrates on the dramatic, ignoring the stabilizing influences in a given situation.

Millions of our young people see little hope or meaning to their future. The resulting frustration has instilled in them an implacable hostility that often finds an outlet for expression in ways quite disturbing to society. To add to the difficulty, there is no longer any satisfactory place to which the disaffected may migrate in large numbers. The western frontier, with its opportunity for constructive flight, has disappeared.

In some of our cities, thousands of persons between eighteen and twenty-five years of age, mostly members of minority groups, have never had a job and have no hope or prospects of holding one. Older people in responsible positions are overtaxed with their business or professional duties. They have little time and energy for strengthening those conditions which form the web of morality that enables a society to function effectively.

For many of our young people, and for Negroes particularly, the slow progress toward the attainment of civil and human rights is incomprehensible. It arouses feelings of hostility that serve as a means of defense against underlying frustration. The legacy of hate being created will not be dissipated for many years. Too many otherwise well-intentioned people do not fully understand the corrosive and disintegrative effects of hostility and rejection.

Many students feel alienated because the times are indeed disturbing and events seem to proceed inexorably against the desires of most individuals. The fact that separate collections of individuals, whether nations or ethnic groups, have incompatible desires does not always seem clear, and, if they are recognized, the means of reconciling them appears weak and ineffectual. They may feel that they are up against some kind of cosmic conspiracy. In the colleges and universities they feel as if they have little to say regarding their own futures. They believe that their opinions regarding their courses and the curriculum are not of interest to the administration and would not be considered even if they were expressed. A considerable number of them do not feel at home in college because they have no sense of belonging; they realize only dimly the significance of what they are doing, and they have no strong beliefs or commitment to any cause. The contrast between the aimless, frustrated, bewildered, perhaps cynical sophomore and the same student one or two years later, when he has found a cause in which he is willing to enlist his efforts, is often almost unbelievable. How to achieve that transition, as well as to help the student endure the anxiety occasioned by uncertainty during the transitional period, should be at the heart of the educational process.

College students (as well as the rest of us) are slowly beginning to realize that the chief obstacles to the realization of their desires lie within themselves rather than in some external impersonal power. We have more material things than we need (in the United States); yet self-centered and selfish forces make equitable distribution difficult. Some people appear too greedy, others too lazy. When we do achieve what we want, the anticipated satisfaction does not come with it. "The green leaves of expectation change to dry ashes in their hands," as one of my friends said of older persons who retire with inadequate preparation.

For the most part, today's students have never had to contend with the implacable conditions generated by extreme poverty, drought, plagues, or economic depression. They have never experienced the need to care for growing plants and domestic animals, duties which demand self-discipline from those who are to be successful, or, in extreme instances, who are to survive. Our youngsters have had to become skillful in manipulating or pleasing people—their parents, friends, or those possessing authority in the community. To them it often seems that when they do not get what they want someone is deliberately withholding it. Frustrations easily become transformed into hostility.

Organized groups promoting hostility against those with whom they disagree have become more open and strong in recent decades than ever before. In their view of life, for every wrong there is a responsible devil. Complicated issues are simplified by finding the person presumably at fault and using him as a scapegoat. Patriotic and religious trappings and slogans give a fake dignity to their efforts. These people become imbued with hatred, use excessively strong language in their criticism of those with whom they disagree, and become victims of their own hostility, just as pathetically and regrettably as do those who have been the subjects of unfair discrimination. Many young people have been caught up in their propaganda.

Another paradox confronting us is that we are suffering at the same time from a surplus of people and a shortage of skilled manpower. We urgently need more teachers, engineers, and scientists, ministers and priests, nurses, physicians, and other members of the health professions (especially in the field of mental illness and health), as well as a large variety of other highly skilled persons. Yet, we know of many young persons in every section of the country who have the necessary intellectual capacity to acquire these needed skills but who are not able to do so. In some instances, the reasons for their inability lie outside themselves—too little money, poor schools, cultural lacks in the communities in which they grew up. In other cases, young people with the requisite ability have been affected by social or peer-group pressures that have resulted in the development of antisocial attitudes which in turn effectively divert them from obtaining the necessary training for effective careers. Some efforts are negated by emotional conflict. Thus the internal, invisible causes operate in concert with external, more apparent influences to deprive society of the services of many persons who could be vastly more productive than they are.

Rapid population increase threatens to prevent social gains in many countries, lowers their standards of living, and further increases the disparities between the "have" and the "have-not" nations. Yet, economic stability and growth in industrialized countries are largely dependent upon continuous expansion of population and increase in the production of both necessities and luxuries. Rapid increases in productivity are closely related to automation, which results, at least temporarily, in fewer work opportunities. A man (or group) replaced by a pushbutton is not likely to welcome the change. Similarly, students resent being considered impersonally, as holes in an IBM card or as an item on a computer tape.

It is becoming increasingly difficult to see a connection between our efforts as individuals and the direction in which society is moving. The good life is within our grasp—yet it constantly eludes us. Factors lying within our psychological make-up constantly delay the realization of the "good society."

As population increases and impersonality becomes common the ordinary person with ideals, manners, and ambition often finds that he seemingly receives no particular notice from those about him, whereas the eccentric in dress, behavior, or morals receives much attention. The "total revolt against soap and society" thus becomes a protest against anonymity and a search for meaning at the same time. Receiving little effective help or understanding from their elders, they become the most conformist of all our youth even as they believe themselves to be in revolt against conformity. Too late they learn that the destruction of all values does not mean that more satisfying ones will automatically replace them.

Unfortunately, many people are in a position to profit from the cultivation of the eccentricities coincident with the struggles of growing up. Those who debase literature with excessive profanity and obscenity, the pornographers masquerading as defenders of free speech, the designers and manufacturers who may profit from exploitation of cupidities of those with low tastes, and the purveyors of "entertainment" all do their part in cheapening the environment in which our young people are expected to acquire satisfying modes of living. They stimulate but do not satisfy.

The young are basically idealistic if given a reasonable opportunity, but their modes of expressing idealism must vary with the issues of the period in which they live. At present, the elimination of social injustice is the "moral equivalent of war" of which William James spoke. The stubborn and (to them) self-defeating resistance which they see many otherwise highminded citizens express against simple justice for minority groups, or for those who are underprivileged from economic, health, education, or other viewpoints, appears willfully selfish. They rush in with criticisms, often in offensive ways. What they lack in facts and manners they make up in zeal and enthusiasm. All too often the result is confusion expressed in power struggles between various groups, rather than willing and disciplined efforts to right the injustices.

The disparity between the demands made upon persons with a high degree of skill or with expert professional training and those who merely have ordinary intelligence or brawn to contribute has never been greater than at present. The shortage of teachers (and abundance of students) is acute and will continue for a long time. In part, because of the relatively low salaries and the high compensation possible in business and industry, many faculty members have added to their income by working as consultants for other organizations; also, many of them feel an obligation to perform public service activities of some kind. This results in keen competition for the time of the best teachers, and a very noticeable effect of such pressure is a reduction in the amount of time that can be devoted to undergraduate teaching. Such teaching is very time consuming and many aspects of it are being delegated to younger colleagues with less experience. When this is done, students may feel cheated.

Many teaching assistants (or fellows) do an excellent job. Without their contributions our colleges would be forced to limit their enrollments drastically. College teaching may have to be even more widely shared than it now is. It can be argued that undergraduate learning will progress much faster if seniors, for example, can be used to teach freshmen. When seniors begin to worry about freshmen they gain a new awareness of themselves. In this role of teachers for the freshmen they gain more understanding of their own teachers. Sanford believes this process of understanding should be speeded up by giving seniors a sense of what it might mean to participate as equals in the activities of the faculty.[1]

There does seem to be a qualitative difference, however, in the contribution that seniors can make to freshman teaching (having recently gone through the same experiences) as compared to what teaching assistants can do for undergraduates when their main responsibility is the attainment of an advanced degree. The latter have frequently had their undergraduate work at another college, their basic emphases are on transmission of subject matter alone, and teaching is for many of them a sideline.

No matter what the reasons, the undergraduate feels cheated when he does not receive personal attention from the more eminent professors in his college. Spreading the influence of the "name" professors by having them lecture to large classes, with graduate students taking charge of the smaller sections, is theoretically desirable, but in fact breaks down when the teaching assistants pay little attention to their responsibilities.

Some of them are, of course, quite capable and diligent and may perform better than a senior professor. In any case, if teaching assistants are to do the bulk of the individual teaching, it is important that they be encouraged to develop good teaching skills and counseling techniques so that they can be more effective in their work with undergraduates. Some resistance to the application of these ideas might be encountered, but it is more likely that this help would be welcomed if the process were carried out imaginatively.

In many of our colleges and universities, the idea persists that anyone who knows a subject well is automatically able to teach effectively. Although competence in understanding still takes precedence over methods of imparting knowledge or cultivating a pleasure in acquiring it, both should be a part of the qualifications of a good teacher. Hostility to schools of education should not be allowed to lead to acceptance of ineffective teaching methods.

Several measures might help students avoid the feeling that they are being cheated. The notion that everything that is learned must first be taught should be examined carefully. Most college students realize that it is their responsibility to acquire an education and that the duty of the college is to develop an environment in which it is possible to acquire one. Much attention must be paid to the students who are uncomfortable unless they are subjected to spoon-feeding methods of teaching. As many devices as possible should be tried which would stimulate the student to be independent. Neglect is not one of them. All teachers should be encouraged to have some contact with undergraduates regularly, the quality of their encounters being of greater significance than the amount of time they can spend with them.

The high esteem in which our colleges and universities are held is nearly matched by the intensity of the criticism many people direct toward their policies and management. Apparently, the belief is widespread that colleges are monolithic and authoritarian institutions whose administrations control and direct all student activities. On the other hand, parents may complain of the lack of direction by the college for their children, not realizing that a college can hardly be expected to "control" several thousand young men and women when two parents cannot force their own child to do what they would like. Students may complain bitterly about their own colleges' inadequacies until they are invited to leave them. Criticisms are energetically voiced by those who do not understand colleges and those who displace their personal problems onto colleges. There is also criticism by reasonable students. Criticism is healthy until it becomes unintelligent and destructive.

The 1964 demonstrations at the University of California at Berkeley were extremely dramatic, occurring as they did in one of the most distinguished universities in the world, and affecting students, faculty members, and administrators who are as capable and high minded as any in existence. But why did it happen there, and could it happen elsewhere? Although the evidence is not conclusive as to why it happened at Berkeley, it certainly seems clear that similar trouble could happen in any of our institutions of higher learning if careful attention is not given to sources of unrest.

At Berkeley, a number of potentially disrupting conditions existed in a closely interwined manner. The University had grown very large, the total enrollment in 1964 being 27,800, with 18,000 undergraduates. The average intelligence was very high. Contact between students and faculty had gradually decreased as the pressure on individual teachers had grown. Advising programs had not been satisfactory to students. The sources of power within the University included the Board of Regents (composed largely of businessmen and ex-officio members), a state-wide University administration, a local University administration, the faculty, and various student organizations and unofficial groups with incomplete knowledge of the entire complex of issues but with firmly fixed notions as to what should be done about them.

Most of the things the students wanted were those traditionally accepted as being desirable in any well run institution. Some demands, however, ran counter to strongly held opinions of conservative sections of the administration, faculty, and students, but particularly of the outside community. Numerous members of the student activist group were far from conventional in their appearance and had somewhat aggressive and often offensive manners. When some of them campaigned for the dispensing of contraceptives on the campus, unrestricted use of drugs such as marihuana, and the right to use obscenities on placards, as a few of them did in the later stages of the demonstrations, the whole situation became critical. The excesses of the relatively few students exhibiting crude manners and regrettably poor judgment brought out correspondingly strong determination on the part of some persons of influence to deal harshly with the offenders.

Some reflections by Gusfield stimulated by the controversy at Berkeley cast additional light on the origins of student unrest.[2] He states that the Berkeley riots symbolize a new period of student action in American universities. As universities become bigger and bigger, communication becomes more difficult. The faculty, administration, and students tend to lose touch with one another. Material success tends to dominate the students' conception of education. As Philip Jacob pointed out, students are relatively little influenced by faculty members' attitudes unless there is close and personal contact.[3] Not only have colleges increased in size, but the faculty has changed, teachers are more cosmopolitan in their orientation, and concepts of liberal arts are weakening in favor of high level professional training. Gusfield thinks we are undergoing a transition from aristocratic to meritocratic education; we are shifting away from aristocratic recruitment toward mass recruitment. The goal seems to be to get everyone into college who can possibly do the work. As more and more people go to college, the disadvantages of not going will increase.

The model of an institution of higher learning is changing from the small liberal arts college to the large impersonal university. Under new circumstances, sentimental ties are apt to be weak. Vocationalism runs rampant. When interaction between students and faculty diminishes, the quality of teaching suffers. Faculty and students live in worlds which seldom touch.

For faculty members, their basic frames of reference are with colleagues in their own disciplines rather than membership in teaching institutions. The main emphasis is on the subject matter and not on teaching itself. Faculty members probably move from institution to institution more than formerly. It is easier to make scapegoats of administrators than of professors. Only during the time spent in the liberal arts college setting is the student free to play with ideas without being strongly limited by his future. This freedom largely disappears in the big universities. Many students develop the idea that college is neither as intellectually exciting nor vocationally meaningful as they had thought it would be. They become progressively alienated. The unrest on the campuses may force administrators and faculty members to look at "the human equation" in the classroom more than they would otherwise have done. As Gusfield concludes "Even professors are beginning to wonder what the students think."[4]

Whatever the message that some of the more active protesters wish to get across, it does not as yet contain many positive factors. Little emphasis is placed on building a better society. Instead their attitude seems to be, "You grown-ups get out of our way." I do not believe that this negative approach represents the thinking of the vast majority of our students, but it is the one getting across to the public.

Many students do not understand the purposes of a liberal education. They consider a college degree a means of increasing their earning power or as a means of access to professional schools. They become uncomfortable and frustrated unless they see each course completed become a part of their vocational training. Nevitt Sanford reminds us that education enlarges the potential in each person and, if successful, makes each individual different from others. Training, on the other hand, tends to process individuals so that they become more alike and can work in concert or in prescribed ways. Training is to some extent the enemy of education and should be postponed as long as we can afford to do so.[5] Many students think of learning not devoted to the acquisition of skills as a waste. Without motivation they become apathetic or unduly critical of the conventional society they can neither understand nor enjoy, and they drop out of college in large numbers.

Those of us who work with college students, whether in deans' offices, counseling agencies, or psychiatric services, know that individual rebellion is very common and in most instances ultimately a good experience. Group rebellion or revolt in the form of mob behavior is quite another matter. It is not clear that such demonstrations ever serve a useful purpose; all too often they bring tragedies to individuals and disrepute to institutions. However, group protests against injustices, conducted in an organized and controlled manner, may be among the most effective instruments for the correction of social evils.

When student demands or protests are met by college authorities with respect, yet countered by explanations of the total range of conflicting pressures that must be considered before decisions are made, the results may be beneficial to everyone. If the demands are unrealistic, the students should be so informed, and at this stage it is imperative that both administrators and faculty members share the responsibility for college policies. Giving in to selfishly conceived demands is likely to encourage expectations that are unrealistic and doomed to later disappointment. A prime purpose of a college is to develop students who are independent in their thinking and willing to embrace new ideas, and to serve as a forum where responsible and informed dissent may be amplified. If too many students in a particular college believe that somebody must give them something, they have become dependent rather than independent.

Many of the causes of student revolt are related to disturbances or deficiencies in students' interpersonal relationships with members of their families or others who mean much to them. When the number of individual students with serious interpersonal problems is not excessive, and each receives a reasonable amount of attention from someone in the college, the likelihood that they will pool their efforts in group rebellion is distinctly diminished. If, however, the number of disturbed youngsters is relatively high, attention paid to counseling or other personal needs of the students is slight, and particularly if there is a person or institution on the campus which excites general dislike, conditions are ripe for an explosion in the form of group action. When such "tinderboxes" exist, a single objectionable act may cause the situation to become critical. Among the possible inciting agents are announcements of new regulations which have not been fully discussed with the persons whom they affect, appointment of a person disliked, failure to reappoint a popular professor, abrupt or apparently unfair or cruel exercise of authority by a police official, or some other episode which incites widespread disapproval. In such instances it is not difficult for clever would-be leaders to exploit the temporary discontent for their own purposes. The best defense of a college in such a situation is the good sense of the great majority of students. As with demagogues generally, they cannot tolerate being understood by large numbers of people.

Where vigorous debate over college policies of any kind is apt to be constructive, struggles for power between two opposing groups, whether they be students and faculty or faculty and administration or administration and students, are apt not to be constructive.

One adamant person in a delicate or combustible situation may be very effective in preventing a solution to debatable or disputed issues. The greater the power held by that individual, the more damaging his fixed attitudes become. If he becomes angry, punitive, or over-excited, the possibilities for undesirable chain reaction effects are multiplied. When all influential persons retain a flexible attitude and willingness to examine all issues, however annoying they may be, the possibilities of resolution are increased.

When a campus gets a reputation of being strife-torn most of the time and a place where excesses in eccentric behavior are commonplace, many students will be repelled from applying to that institution, and the morale of faculty members will be lowered because of the disagreeable controversy. Whereas some faculty members feel somewhat exploited if they are expected to pay attention to the personal needs or feelings of students, they may perhaps fare even worse if neglect of students results in stimulating their contentious and anti-intellectual characteristics.

One observer with access to many sources of student opinion gives this optimistic note and a warning: "If one says that students share a mood of protest, it must quickly be added that this protest is far from an idealogical nihilism. It is, in fact, more nearly an assertion of a standard than a protest of another. It is a positive response to a negative social condition, a desire to contribute to tomorrow when the tomorrows are reserved to the care of others. Unless this responsive mood is welcomed as much as if it came from an (older) adult, it may too easily find an alternative mode of expression as a distant, excessive protest with which there will be little communication and a lot of confusing noise."[6]

What are the methods for dealing with student unrest of any type? Obviously, there is no way to avoid rebellion. Nor would it be desirable to do so. Impatience with injustice and any practices which demean the dignity of man is an attribute which we should try to develop and encourage in our students. But such impatience should not be so impulsive as to be destructive of individuals or ideals.

Administration and faculty members will find that constructive rebellion and subsequent maturation are facilitated if they treat students with scrupulous fairness at all times, listen to their complaints, no matter how trivial, and act with consistency on matters of student concern. Good personal relations should be developed with as many students as possible. Promises should be made only when they can be kept. The standards of the institution should be appropriately explicit, but rules that cannot possibly be enforced should be avoided.

Even if temporarily disconcerting, the renaissance of student interest in social and political questions is a very encouraging phenomenon. Only a decade ago, we were deploring their apathy. Not only must the faculty be willing to accept and facilitate change—we are obligated to see that progress is truly helpful, not simply a change from one set of evils to another.

In the past, the young were greatly outnumbered and their orderly transition from youth to adulthood could be facilitated by many older persons. With the older generation's relative diminution in numbers, and perhaps also of influence, it has become far more difficult to aid youth in developing a sense of meaning and purpose and in giving them a system of values for their own guidance.

Our society has taken too lightly the task of determining

which of our values are worthwhile and of demonstrating how they may be transmitted from the older to the younger generations. We have done reasonably well with small groups of young people, but not with the vast bulk of them. Obviously, we should not attempt to tell our college students what they should believe, do, and say, but we should be able to do more than we have thus far in convincing them that retaining the old values that have been useful and shaping better goals and ideals in light of the older values is preferable to throwing all the old values away because some of them are not upheld in practice.

In academic circles, as elsewhere, we have seen strong attacks on the system of ethics, if it can be termed a system, called the Puritan (or Protestant) ethic. The "wear it out, eat it up, make it do" attitude toward life is inconsistent with many aspects of our present society, and if practiced would be catastrophic to our automobile manufacturers, farmers, and all those who prosper from early obsolescence of their products. Similarly, the overly stern and punitive aspects of behavior regulation practiced in earlier times have lost their attractiveness and effectiveness. Yet, those who have been most vocal in their attacks on the Puritan ethic have not yet succeeded in developing an alternative that has its good points without its excesses. Our young people have heard much more discussion of their rights than of their responsibilities. Many of them have been confronted with relatively little restraint during childhood; and not much emphasis has been placed on their duties to others. As a result, they have not learned the principle expressed so cogently by Judge Learned Hand, "A society in which men recognize no check upon their freedom soon becomes a society where freedom is the possession of only a savage few."[7]

The liberation of man from the necessity of prolonged hard work permits him the luxury of leisure. Leisure time should allow exploration of music, the arts, literature, philosophy, religion— the pursuits and endeavors of civilization. The fact is, however, that for many persons leisure seems to increase tension, boredom, apathy, and unhappiness, and to produce a sense of the lack of meaning and purpose. Teachers feel guilty unless they feel overworked. Students may not know what to do with leisure when they get it.

Although it has always been the custom of older people to view young people with some dismay and apprehension, the present situation probably calls for even more concern than usual. Not only do our young people form a larger proportion of the population than previously, but they have at their disposal vastly more effective means of expressing their opinions. Through rapid means of communication and transportation and by new modes of group action they can quickly throw a community into turmoil. Attitudes toward authority have become less respectful than formerly, possibly because some who possess it have used it so unwisely.

Indeed, the whole range of attitudes toward authority has undergone considerable change during the last few years. Respect for police has never been high but may now be lower than ever before as a result of the brutality which has been rampant during civil rights demonstrations. Some state governors have forfeited national respect because of their activities in defense of segregation, even as they have temporarily won support in their own states from those who favor it. Disrespectful attitudes toward the chief executive of the nation have always been strong—they are certainly not diminishing. Religious organizations have lost some of their capacity to instill respect. When parents are no longer able to command obedience, the young person may reasonably conclude that he is bound by no rules.

Unfortunately, respect for and understanding of authority is inadequate among persons of all ages, not just among the young. Respect for law and order cannot be inculcated in the young unless it is practiced by adults. Developing such respect is a vast but uncompleted task for society, the colleges and universities included.

The social scientists, including psychiatrists, have too often assumed that studying values is as far as their responsibilities go. To take a stand or express a preference would be unscientific and impair one's standing with one's colleagues. This attitude is also exhibited by many faculty members of other disciplines, perhaps in a manner which does not do justice to their convictions. It is almost as if they were somewhat embarrassed to have deep commitments to one system of values in preference to another.

The social scientists (and psychiatrists) who are deeply committed to the elevation of value standards are distinctly in a minority.

Because of issues considered in this chapter, as well as for many other reasons the question of what we should be doing about our young people should be considered one of society's main concerns. As Sanford has said, "All the resources of society should be utilized for the development of children and youth. This, I should say, is mainly what a society is for. If suitable agencies and institutions do not exist they will have to be created."[8] One wonders why we are surprised at the current crisis in meaning and values and why we have not foreseen and planned more effectively for the training of the increasing number of young people whom we knew would now be on the threshold of adulthood. We find it difficult to understand why our young people seem to reject so many of our familiar values, and we do not appreciate sufficiently the fact that most of us have not given clear evidence that we believe in them ouselves.

REFERENCES

1. SANFORD, N.: *College and Character*. New York, Wiley, 1964, pp. 293-294.
2. GUSFIELD, J.: Beyond Berkeley: High noon on campus. *Transaction*, 2:3-7, 1965.
3. JACOB, P. E.: *Changing Values in College*. New York, Harper, 1957, pp. 7-8.
4. GUSFIELD J.: *Op. cit.*, p. 7.
5. SANFORD, N.: Factors related to the effectiveness of student interaction with the college social system. In: *Higher Education and Mental Health*, B. Barger, and E. E. Hall, Eds., Proceedings of a Conference, University of Florida, 1963, p. 10.
6. LIEBERT, R.: The protest mood of students. *YMCA Intercollegian*, September 1965.
7. DILLIARD, I., Ed.: *The Spirit of Liberty, Papers and Addresses of Learned Hand*. New York, Knopf, 1952, p. 190.
8. SANFORD, N.: *College and Character*. Wiley, New York, 1964, p. 281.

CHAPTER IX

SEXUAL MORALITY—THE DILEMMA
OF THE COLLEGES

T ODAY, YOUNG PEOPLE are exposed to more sexual stimuli than ever before. Our drama and literature have become increasingly explicit in their treatments of sex, as have contemporary journalism and television. Advertising media use pressures and appeals which are essentially sexual in nature to encourage product consumption; emphasis is placed on glamour, physical attractiveness, social success, etc., and in turn these qualities are equated with happiness and the good life.

The mass media (movies, television, radio, advertising) concentrate on the most superficial of values, usually to the exclusion of the more basic, meaningful, complex, and constant issues of human life. The trend away from Victorian attitudes and toward greater honesty is a healthy one. But the opposite side of the coin is a continual barrage of material that is sexually provocative and also difficult to detect because (a) it is often manipulated in a subtle manner, and (b) it exploits human assumptions and psychological forces of which most of us are unaware (i.e., which are unconscious). Since their appeal is largely irrational, these pressures are extremely difficult to deal with.

Much has been said recently of the various aspects of the "American sexual revolution" and the weakening of the traditional sexual "double standard," the increased number of women who work, etc.; social (and, by extension, sexual) patterns *are* undergoing change, as indeed they have been throughout history. There is talk of the development of a new morality; one hears that more honesty about sexual relations now exists; that fidelity, not virginity, is the important element in male-female relationships, and that one is not really mature until he has had affairs with members of the opposite sex. There is nothing particularly new about these ideas except that (1) they are being advanced with increasing urgency by a wide variety of persons and agencies, and (2) most people are so confused about the various conflicting arguments that they don't know what to believe.

Some parents express strong disapproval or horror at the new trends, others accept them (probably with some misgivings when their own children are involved), while the majority vacillate inconsistently from one point of view to another. Their desire for children to make early and successful marriages causes some parents to accept compromises with their ideals in order to achieve this goal.

Those who try to develop or uphold responsible standards of sexual behavior are usually chided by their sophisticated friends. They are told that they can't turn the clock back, that freedom is here to stay, that conventional morality is obsolete. What then, should be the position of one who wishes the best possible kind of life for himself and for all those who come after him?

Some regulation and control of sexual activities has been found necessary by all societies. Unrestrained sexual freedom soon results in freedom only for the powerful and the unscrupulous, and only temporarily even for them. What is desirable insofar as sex (like many other areas of life) is concerned is a development of a freedom in which we can grow and mature, enjoy ourselves and have a sense of fulfillment, experience appropriate relations with members of the opposite sex without behaving destructively in the process. Appropriate expression of sexual drives (both in the specific and more general senses) is necessary both for happiness and continuation of the race, and is one of the most civilizing of all human influences.

Sex and marriage are inextricably intertwined, and in turn are central to the establishment of strong family life. Without the latter, the rearing of children becomes incredibly difficult, and the results often are unfortunate.

The type of sexual morality we develop is therefore related to the kind of society we want now and in the future. Lowering of sexual restraints is usually accompanied by lowered standards of behavior in other areas. Ideally, there should be reasonable harmony between those who base their standards on ethical values and those whose beliefs derive from religious considerations, even when the two sets of assumptions do not coincide.

Definite standards of sexual morality help those who adhere to them and those who violate them. The latter may learn from their mistakes if they realize clearly why they were penalized. When there are no standards, when everything is considered relative, confusion prevents people from making realistic decisions about their own behavior.

Some students of ethics say that we are much more moral now than we used to be; i.e., we used to be moral because we were afraid to be immoral, whereas now we are moral because we choose to be. Ideally, our young people should have the kind of education concerning the issues involved in sexual behavior that would enable them, after a full and thoughtful consideration of all the issues involved, to make their own decisions as to what they should or should not do. They should not be forced into behavior which they do not themselves want, and for which they are not ready, by unduly strong pressures from their peers or the mass media.

Because of reticence in speaking about sex, doubt as to what to say, and firmly held divergent and contradictory attitudes, there has thus far been a notable lack of success in finding a reliable and practical way of conveying accurate information about sexual matters in our schools and colleges. There is no general agreement on what should be included in such presentations, how it should be presented, or how to keep objective data and moralizing separate.

Sexual activity before marriage might be thought of as a spectrum; on one extreme is a person who has any kind of relationship with anyone he chooses at any time and with no reservations whatsoever; on the other end of the spectrum is the person who permits no physical intimacy of any kind until marriage. Either type of individual is heading for much unhappiness, even possibly for disaster.

College students are at an age at which sexual preoccupation is as high as at any other time in life. The young men are at the peak of physical sexual desire, while the young women are possibly more concerned with the choice of a suitable husband. It is quite possible that the basic emotions of young men and women are quite similar, though cultural pressures suggest that the men should be more openly concerned with physical sexual satisfaction while the women should be preoccupied with finding a suitable marriage partner. There is much opinion among those who work with college students that attitudes of many young women are changing toward that formerly thought characteristic of young men—that of valuing physical sexual satisfaction for its own sake. This would not imply any lessening of the importance of securing a desirable mate.

College officials may comfort themselves with the realization that their students would be having sexual problems even if they were not in college. Their behavior would possibly be more free than in college, though with some conspicuous exceptions. The main difference is that in the partial control exercised by the college there is an opportunity, not as favorable elsewhere, to encourage among students the development of thoughtful and responsible attitudes toward sexual behavior and the development of subsequent satisfying family life. Unfortunately, most colleges are unable to make use of this opportunity because of lack of qualified personnel and inadequate support from parents, faculty, and the opinion-molders of society.

It is not surprising that in a society that places a high value on material possessions and immediate sensual gratifications some young people become involved in sexual behavior during their college years that will be a source of distress to them afterward. Pleasant relations with many friends of both sexes form one of the important aspects of the entire college experience. Learning how to get along with numerous members of the opposite sex is an excellent way for a young person to improve his chances of getting along well with one of them in marriage. The tendency to short-circuit this process by rushing into intimate relations before it is socially and legally appropriate (in part because of social pressures from their own peers and from society generally) may be a handicap to later success in marriage. At the very least, it is highly desirable that each student be encouraged to live in accordance with his own ideals, make his own choices and learn from his own mistakes, rather than become a puppet with someone else pulling the strings.

The question is often asked of psychiatrists as to whether coeducational or sexually segregated schools are the most conducive to the development of reasonable standards of sexual behavior, or in negative terms, which arrangement is most disadvantageous to mature emotional development. Current evidence does not indicate the superiority of one arrangement over another. It is a matter of personal preference for the individual to decide for himself.

In their analysis of the pressures on college students toward premarital relations, Mitchell and Bruyn state that many students fail to see the need for responsible action and do not appreciate the penalties which may result from their irresponsibility.[1] The old deterrents of fear of pregnancy and venereal disease are gone; new ones have not appeared which have been convincing to them. The authors points out that "through ignorance, weird reasoning, or a certain bravado, most girls ignore contraceptives, and then wonder why they should be so unlucky as to get pregnant." Many girls, as well as their boy friends, feel that society, and the medical profession particularly, should disregard moral and legal considerations and rescue them from their predicaments by means of illegal abortions.

Morgan, a minister serving as a chaplain for college students, suggests that college health officers may not be using religious counselors as effectively as they might because they see them as being moralistic and prone to pass judgments on a couple who have learned that the girl is pregnant.[2] He suggests that with the lessening of the fears of pregnancy and disease (and detection) "we now have a chance to build morality on the foundation it should have had in the first place; on some criteria of satisfying human relationships."

In addition to the usual influences pushing young people into sexual relations (biological impulse, a declaration of freedom, etc.), Morgan believes that there has been a frightening crisis in meaning. We have given young people little reason to think about moral standards. They are starved for meaningful relationships. There is a notable lack of models of healthy adult relationships. Exploitation of the individual becomes commonplace as impersonality becomes the social rule.

The most damaging of the complications of premarital sexual relations is pregnancy. For this eventuality, there is no solution without disadvantages. The possibilities open to the girl include prompt marriage, carrying the child to term and placing it for adoption or caring for it herself, or abortion, either legal or criminal.

Legal abortions are seldom authorized. Ordinarily they cannot be obtained without an involved procedure in which two or more physicians, the operating surgeon, the director of the hospital, and a law enforcement officer (district attorney) all agree that the procedure is necessary to save the life, health, or reason of the mother. Obviously, few young women meet such qualifications. Regulations vary widely from state to state but none are particularly liberal.

Criminal abortions may be secured relatively easily if one "knows the ropes" and has considerable money. Various unethical practitioners may set themselves up in this business and make a great deal of money until a mistake results in the death of the woman, following which they must disappear for a while. Abortions may sometimes be secured outside the United States under reasonably safe conditions, but these are not easy to procure except in the case of a few exceptional situations relatively close to the border (which are seldom permanent).

Many women think that having an abortion ends the matter; the psychological trauma may be severe, whether the abortions are legal or illegal.

In a study made on pregnant, unmarried university students from the period 1958 to 1963 at the University of Edinburgh an attempt was made to determine the mental health status of these women before pregnancy occurred.[3] There were fifty-seven of them in all. This group was compared with another fifty-seven who were chosen at random from the register of students. The fifty-seven pregnancies occurred in a group of 1,422 women. Their ages ranged from eighteen to twenty-seven, and all but six were under twenty-two years of age. Of the fifty-seven pregnant unmarried students, twenty-six (or 45.6%) had consulted their physicians with a conspicuous psychiatric disability during the first year at the University, compared with nine (or 15.8%) of the controls. It was concluded that not only did neurotic factors play a significant part in the pregnancies, but that these were manifested prior to conception.

In the course of the discussion, a physician made this observation: "Many girls at seventeen are ready to form a permanent sex relationship, whereas many boys of nineteen are not. A girl of seventeen rejected by her nineteen-year-old lover argues that 'I am rejected as a woman; I am a failure.' She moves on from boyfriend to boyfriend seeking permanent acceptance and is given the brushoff after a year or so by each, as none of them is ready to settle down permanently with any girl. As they move on from victory to victory, proving their own manhood, she progresses from defeat to defeat. Her whole validity as a woman is destroyed and she reckons herself as a failure."

Homosexuality is always a difficult problem in a college community, as elsewhere, because its nature is not well understood. Some homosexual behavior is present in any large community and it is quite impossible to eliminate all individuals who become involved in it, even if that were desirable. Rather than taking a punitive attitude toward homosexual preoccupation and behavior, the psychiatrist assumes that it is an evidence of incomplete emotional maturation. Psychotherapy should be recommended when practicable because many young persons, particularly, can be helped to develop the more mature heterosexual orientation. Older persons may also be helped by psychotherapy if they wish to change their attitudes or behavior, but the possibilities of effecting a lasting change decrease with age.

A good practical rule to follow is to treat homosexuality and heterosexuality similarly. Whatever a particular person does in private, with a consenting individual, is his own responsibility. If he invades the privacy of another person, and that person protests, society must take corrective action. This is true whether the attempted seduction is of a homosexual or heterosexual nature. Any student who reports private behavior in a confidential counseling situation must have his confidence respected. In effect this is an expression of distress and a cry for help; the individual should be referred to the best professional help available.

Some college officials are so sensitive about their institution's reputation that they feel that any person with homosexual inclinations should be eliminated from their organization. A few demand breach of confidence from those who know of homosexual activities through confidential sources, but no ethical counselor or psychiatrist would comply with such a request. Occasionally an unwise college official will instruct his police force to engage in seductive activities to entrap those who may be homosexually inclined. This practice can only be condemned. Excessive efforts to "weed out" homosexuality can lead to more damage to a college and its reputation than homosexual behavior itself brings about.

A common excuse for drastic action against a person known to be homosexual, even if he has committed no breach of public decency, is that his attitudes may spread to others. In the college age group this is not a serious problem. Anyone who has achieved a mature heterosexuality finds the advantages too great to be voluntarily given up. Anyone who engages in openly seductive activities, whether student or faculty member, has lost his usefulness in the college community and should be held accountable for his actions. Whether he should be suspended or discharged is dependent upon many factors peculiar to each case. In any case, efforts should be made to aid the individual in his own rehabilitation, wherever he may go subsequently. The fact that a medical reason exists for his disability does not excuse him from responsibility for his behavior.

Other types of sexual deviation include exhibitionism (inappropriate exposure of the genitalia), transvestitism (morbid impulse to wear clothing of the opposite sex), and voyeurism (sexual pleasure through looking at the genitals of another). These kinds of behavior provide sexual gratification in the absence of a physical relationship and represent a severe inadequacy of sexual development in those persons who show such symptoms. The determining factors producing such behavior have their origins in childhood, and the individual cannot control his actions by will power alone. Thus, punishment has no effect in controlling such deviations; psychiatric treatment is always desirable if the individual can accept such help.

During the last few years much interest has been focused on sexual practices in the colleges, interest stimulated both by the demands of students for greater freedom in this area and by confusion on the parts of parents and college officials as to what the proper standards of behavior should be. It is quite difficult for parents and children to talk together frankly about sexual matters because of the great gulf in experience between the two generations. The background of our present college generation is very different from that of their parents. Social change was quite rapid during the time the parents of today were maturing, but is even more so at present.

Communication between older and younger members of college communities is also hampered by many factors: lack of concensus as to what the central issues are, criticism of those who become interested in the subject, and lack of competent persons to hold discussion groups, among others.

The sexual behavior of college students may be changing in the direction of practices formerly attributed to members of lower socio-economic groups.[4] Reliable data on which to base such an opinion is not yet conclusive, but all general observations suggest this to be true. There is thought to be not only a qualitative change in sexual practices but also an acceleration in such behavior. What was thought to be characteristic behavior at eighteen or twenty years of age may now be observed in persons sixteen or eighteen or even younger.

Three points of view regarding sexual behavior generally obtain: 1) the traditional morality; 2) the new morality; and 3) amorality. In the first of these, traditional morality, the following principles are considered fundamental:

a.   Renunciation or control of instinctual gratification permits a reasonable degree of civilization (Freud).

b.   Restraint tends to aid in developing a capacity for thoughtfulness concerning the welfare of others, particularly in a parental sense. Restraint aids in the sublimation of sexual energies.

c. Marriage becomes one of life's most cherished institutions when sexual restraint is practiced.

d. The total moral fiber of a society is strengthened if sexual standards are maintained, weakened when sexual standards are ignored.

e. Young people need help in controlling their strong impulses during their formative years.

In the new morality, fidelity and consideration of others occupy a very high place. Physical sex is supposed to occur only after the establishment of friendship and love. Exploitation of the sexual partner is very much opposed. A high ethical component is apparent in the thinking of those who adhere to this general view, even though concomitant behavior may not be in accordance with that approved by traditionalists and many religious groups.

In the third approach, the central belief is that no restrictions are needed. If sexual impulses are allowed free rein, tension, anxiety, and frustration will be lowered, and happiness, satisfaction in living, and effectiveness increased. The main problem for those who hold this point of view is that of persuading other persons to accept this way of behaving.

Obviously, no one is an exemplar of any one of these three points of view to the total exclusion of the others. Any particular individual may move from one point of view to another, or he may adhere to one point of view and act as if he upheld another. It is this discrepancy between outer appearance and private behavior that is confusing to many persons, young and old alike.

In the past, sexual behavior has been regulated in varying degrees by religious teachings and customs based on them, and by fear of disaster if something goes wrong, such as detection, disease, or pregnancy. These deterrents to free sexual behavior have become somewhat weakened, especially during the last few decades, for reasons familiar to everyone. At the same time, there does not appear to have been any major moral breakdown. This suggests that the present generation of young people is fully as moral as any in the past, although for different reasons.

College officials are very much concerned about certain key issues associated with sexual behavior. For example, pressures toward experience which the young person does not wish and for which he is not yet ready may be unduly effective. A certain "bandwagon" effect occurs when peer group pressures push young people into such behavior. Frequently these pressures become so strong that a young person subject to them may feel guilty for not indulging in behavior currently popular, just as he may feel guilty for doing so if his training has been a conventional or traditional one.

Parental attitudes in general are not consistent enough for any guidelines or policy. Although opinions regarding sexual behavior are usually very firmly held, parents sometimes favor and at other times oppose free sexual expression. Furthermore, when college administrators are called upon to take definite action in a given situation, there is a considerable tendency to blame such officials for their attempts at restoring order rather than to look at the original source of difficulty. Furthermore, the more divergent the views of proper behavior become, the greater the intolerance exhibited by individuals toward those with views with which they do not agree.

Freedom of choice is desired for all students, but when peer group pressures and the bandwagon effect become too strong, the individual may be deprived of this freedom.

I believe it is correct to assert that most college administrators do not wish to have a series of complicated and specific rules regarding behavior in this area, realizing that attempts at enforcement create many new problems. They do not wish to develop a spy system, since the main purpose of the college experience is to enable students to develop the ability to make their own decisions, hopefully wise ones. Most administrators are averse to imposing their personal views on others, varying as they do from person to person, institution to institution, and section to section in the country. Administrators also cannot and do not wish to ignore public sentiment in the communities surrounding the colleges.

Current emphasis on all aspects of sex in novels, plays, and the mass media of communication may enable parents, teachers, and others to become more honest about sexual education than has been possible up to now.

At the present time, it seems to me that the following (perhaps insoluble) problems prevent the promotion of a satisfactory kind of sexual education. Religious views vary among sects as well as in different parts of the country. Contraception is not completely reliable no matter what assurances some people may give. For college students, this reliability may be impaired by conscious maneuvering on the part of one partner to produce pregnancy. The strong views of parents, either in the direction of freedom of sexual behavior or of control, are not expressed in such a way as to be of much help. Those who have a vested interest in pornography are very ingenious in developing excellent arguments to prevent interference in their moneymaking activities. College administrators value freedom and dislike censorship. Drawing the line between these attitudes and the desire to be helpful in guiding the development of young people into channels which will not be destructive to their future is a very delicate matter. There is no consensus as to appropriate means of furthering sex education, not only at the college level but at all stages of development. Variations in attitudes toward sexual education in different sections of the country make it almost impossible for any widespread program to be adopted. Not the least of the difficulties is that anyone working seriously for improved sexual adaptation almost invariably becomes an object of ridicule for his associates and others in the community.

Once a program is agreed upon, the question then arises of who will carry it out. Should it be done by parents, physicians, members of the clergy, marital counselors, faculty members, or some other group? If persons in any of these groups are willing to undertake this task, then how shall they be trained? How is it possible to separate the giving of factual information from moralizing?

One might suppose that guidance should come from physicians, but this is not necessarily the case. Some physicians appear to believe that knowledge of anatomy and physiology is all that is needed. Others give the impression that the desirable course is to disseminate contraceptive advice and materials widely and assume that students' sexual behavior is of no concern to the colleges. Very few medical schools give any encouragement to their students to become proficient in marital counseling, not because they do not consider it desirable but because they do not know how. Furthermore the demands on medical students' time are constantly increasing, making anything more than attaining proficiency in the vocabulary of medicine during the four under-graduate years an impossibility.

College officials may be reticent about imposing their views on others, but they do wish to make it crystal clear that they uphold high standards of personal behavior just as they uphold intel-lectual integrity. They want to encourage as much thoughtfulness in this area of behavior as in any other. They wish to develop the kind of behavior which will not bring unnecessary unhappiness or disaster to young people as they fashion a way of life which will strengthen rather than weaken family life.

In my opinion, no particular point of view can be forced on young people, but there should be full and frank discussion in families, in groups, between couples, and between older and younger colleagues in the colleges. If students are given answers without any real awareness of the issues, they will not be helped very much. If, however, a program is developed which will enable them to achieve a keen awareness of the issues involved, they may come up with better answers than our generation has been able to evolve.

After all, the problem is of more significance to young people than those of the older generation. It is up to them to determine what kind of a world they want their children to live in. As they discuss sexual issues, it is desirable that they recall the nature of the training they experienced and the embarrassing situations they encountered in their childhood, while relating these experi-ences to their present problems. Finally, they should project their thoughts into the future in terms of developing attitudes toward sex which will be helpful as they begin to raise their own children. This three-dimensional approach to the problem encourages some objectivity, instead of the rather intense urgency with which most young adolescents and early adults view such problems.

Unfortunately, those who guide the policies of institutions get little help from parents, as I have already stated, because of the confusion and variety of their views, but I fear that they get even less from the faculty. There is a tendency to leave all such matters to the dean's office and to give inadequate support to the idea that integrity confined to intellectual matters is quite insufficient and should be extended to all facets of behavior.

Even though the colleges are not *in loco parentis* to their students in the literal sense, they do have a responsibility to encourage them to adopt reasonable standards of behavior. There is no compelling reason for college administrators to be intimidated by the accusation that they are "upholding middle-class morals." Standards of morality and means by which they are determined and transmitted from one generation to another are proper and necessary subjects for continuing discussion between students and faculty members.

For parents, religious leaders, college officials and all others who have a responsibility for late adolescents and young adults in secondary schools and colleges, some standards or ideals of behavior are desirable. Let us first examine the principle, "All premarital sexual intercourse is undesirable." Deviations from that code of behavior have every imaginable variety, ranging from rape or the production of a child with illegitimate parents (at the most regrettable end of the spectrum of undesirable activities) to intercourse between engaged couples who expect to marry soon and who can marry at once if pregnancy occurs (at the least undesirable end). In each instance of departure from the ideal, the individual does so knowing of its undesirability and with an awareness of possible consequences. If unpleasant developments follow, he is in a position to learn from his experience; there is no one on whom he can reasonably project blame.

Let us assume another principle: "Premarital sexual relations are undesirable for those who are immature or cannot undertake the responsibility for a possible child, but for those who are mature and responsible, they are enriching and enobling." Immediately, the couple considering such relations must classify themselves, just at the time when it is only logical that they should be optimistic. It is easy to guess what the decision will be. When tragedy ensues, as it occasionally does, who can wonder that they are confused about society's inconsistent attitudes toward them?

Until we resolve our own confusions, we will not be in a favorable position to help our younger colleagues make their ways along the complex paths of development to sexual maturity. The experiences in our college psychiatric and counseling services lead us to believe that those who ignore the conventional standards are no more happy or effective than those who observe them. In fact, I believe that they have more depression, anxiety, agitation, and other inhibiting emotional conflict than those who manage to adhere to their ideals.

A large proportion of the younger students who come from families with reasonable ideals feel more comfortable if limits are set, some guidelines evident, and some one who cares enough about them to help them avoid disaster than if no one seems to care what they do.

As college officials, we are more concerned with the quality of future marriages and the family life they make possible than with any particular physical act in which either partner may have been involved. Of course, this does not imply that the nature and extent of sexual activities before marriage is irrelevant to the success of that marriage.

If we are to progress in making sense out of this important area of personal development, we will need the sympathetic understanding and support of parents, faculty members, and the students themselves. There should then follow innumerable personal discussions, seminars, and other procedures for transmitting accurate information. At the same time, the complex issues associated with choice of behavior should be explored. Opinions concerning sexual behavior should be expressed, but not be put forth as scientific facts.

Sexual education and the formation of standards of sexual morality are not separable from other aspects of personal maturation, nor should they be unduly circumscribed as they are pursued in the colleges. The goal should be that of aiding each student to develop a healthy personality in which sexuality plays a constructive and satisfying part, rather than being considered undignified and regrettable.

Erikson poses the alternative modes of behavior perceptively and explicitly when he says: "For, whatever the partial satisfactions and partial abstinences that characterize premarital sex life in various cultures— whether the pleasure and pride of forceful genital activity without commitment, or of erotic states without genital consummation, or of disciplined and devoted delay—ego development uses the psychosexual powers of adolescence for enhancing a sense of style and identity."[5]

"Disciplined and devoted delay" is at the heart of what we should be helping our young people to achieve so that their marriages and accompanying family life can be as rich and rewarding as possible. Ideally, each college should have a program to aid its students in obtaining sound knowledge of sexual attitudes and behavior and of how sexuality may contribute to, rather than interfere with, their progress in college. This calls for collaborative efforts on the part of deans, physicians (including psychiatrist), counselors of all kinds, and all students. This has not been done at all in most colleges and not done well in any. Colleges have been accused of trying to control sexual behavior by keeping their students in ignorance, but this is absurd. The unfortunate fact is that as yet college officials have inadequate knowledge of what constitutes a good program, and too little support from their colleagues and from parents when they attempt to organize one.

A college psychiatrist has a dual responsibility insofar as the sexual components of development are concerned. He is desirous of promoting healthy sexuality among students; he also believes (with the college administration and parents) that extreme and inappropriate behavior is both dangerous and damaging. He hopes to promote a high degree of sexual morality among students, but if he moralizes he loses his influence to help them. Should he attempt to draw general inferences or conclusions from his clinical experience, they may be incorrect because he does not know how typical or atypical his observations are when compared with the sexual experiences of those students who have not sought help.

A practical escape from the psychiatrist's dilemma is to keep himself as well informed as possible regarding sexual practices but to use this knowledge in two separate ways. He tries to help each person who seeks aid from him with complete observance of the rules of privacy and without taking a judgmental attitude. The student should have confidence that nothing he divulges will ever be used against him. In his second compartment of activities the college psychiatrist should feel free to express his opinions as to what constitutes appropriate behavior to whomever he chooses, taking his chances with the reactions of those who may disagree with him. Whereas in dealing with patients he is not free to make use of any specific knowledge he may acquire, in his public utterances the principle of academic freedom should apply. Even so, the less publicity given to his work with students, at least insofar as the press is concerned, the more effective he is likely to be over a long period. Material that is essential to the success of group discussions on sexual maturation is not suitable for public discussion in newspapers, particularly when the writing is done by incompetent and sensation-seeking reporters.

In many colleges, pressure is being applied by some students to persuade college health services to dispense contraceptives to unmarried students and to supervise their use. Some physicians may be somewhat sympathetic to this view, looking upon an undesired pregnancy as being a greater tragedy than the possible harmful effects of seeming to condone premarital sexual relations. A college health director cannot avoid developing a policy to meet the divergent pressures on him and his colleagues. The policy of the Harvard University Health Services is as follows: "Members of the college health service may discuss with students any aspect of their private lives about which there is any concern. However, supervision of contraceptive practices of unmarried students is not an appropriate function for a college health service. To do so would suggest approval of premarital relations, imply that the college assumes responsibility which does not properly belong to it, and run counter to the wishes of the great majority of parents."

In the Group for the Advancement of Psychiatry's Report on *Sex and the College Student,* a series of excellent suggestions are made regarding the development of guidelines for college policy toward sexuality.[6] These include the creation of regulations or customs that will encourage informal contacts but maintain some measure of external control, avoiding students' being burdened with too much freedom which they cannot handle. Regulations should be designed to shift increasing responsibility on students as they grow older; the eighteen-year-old needs more setting of limits than the twenty-one-year-old senior. Students should participate in policy development, though with the clear understanding that ultimate responsibility rests with the administration. The attitude of the college toward sex on the campus should be explicit; the college cannot control the sexual behavior of its students but it can define acceptable and unacceptable behavior. Whether one does or does not agree with the suggestions made in the Report, any college official or teacher who is confronted by such problems—and all of them are—will be greatly rewarded by a study of this Report.

REFERENCES

1. MITCHELL, G. M., AND BRUYN, H. B.: Sex behavior in the young adult: The perspective of a college health service. *J. Amer. Coll. Health Ass., 13*:173-178, 1964.
2. MORGAN, G. P.: Sex behavior in the modern young adult. *J. Amer. Coll. Health Ass., 13*:179-186, 1964.
3. KIDD, C. B., GIEL, R., AND BROWN, J. B.: The antecedent mental health of pregnant unmarried women. Proceedings of the British Student Health Association, Oxford, July 1964, pp. 51-59.
4. KINSEY, A. C., POMEROY, W. B., MARTIN, C. E., AND GEBHARD, P. H.: *Sexual Behavior in the Human Female.* Philadelphia, Saunders, 1953, pp. 293-296.
5. ERIKSON, E. H., Ed.: *Youth: Change and Challenge.* New York, Basic Books, 1965, p. 9.
6. Group for the Advancement of Psychiatry: *Sex and the College Student,* GAP Report No. 60 (Publication office 104 E. 25th St., New York), October 1965.

CHAPTER X

COUNSELING BY FACULTY MEMBERS

IN THIS CHAPTER, special attention will be given to the role of the teacher who is not a professional counselor but who is vitally interested in the total maturation of his students—intellectual, emotional, social, and physical. He is concerned not so much with the extremes of behavior (physical illness, crippling emotional conflict) but with the great variety of quandaries faced and choices to be made by all students. Just as every professional counselor (clinical psychologist, social worker, or psychiatrist) should keep in mind the primacy of the intellectual goals of the institution, so should every teacher keep in mind the tremendous influence of the feelings and emotions of his students as they struggle to increase their intellectual capacity and motivation.

In the United States, counseling programs have become well established in many institutions. The majority of these programs have been developed by psychologists. Among the eminent persons who have made major contributions to the theory and practice of counseling are Arbuckle,[1] Bordin,[2] Rogers,[3, 4, 5] Super,[6] Tyler,[7] and Williamson.[8, 9] Their principal publications serve to open up the extensive literature of counseling.

Training programs for counselors are numerous and their graduates do the great majority of professional counseling in American colleges and universities. College psychiatrists owe much to this group, probably more than most of them realize. The work of counselors, valuable as it has been, was incomplete without the viewpoint of psychiatrists—an emphasis on the more serious and long-standing emotional conflicts that eventually result in severe emotional and mental illness if not resolved or minimized. The entry of psychiatrists into the college health

166

services, and then into collaborative relations with all other counselors, may be viewed as an attempt to meet the needs of those students with quite serious problems.

No attempt is made in this book to summarize the theory and practice of counseling; this has been done well and often in the references just cited and elsewhere.

During the last few decades, and especially since World War II, there has been a rapid growth of psychiatric counseling connected with college health services. Publications of Fry,[10] Farnsworth,[11] Wedge,[12] and others illustrate the basic points of view and the goals of college psychiatrists. Three reports by the Committee on the College Student of the Group for the Advancement of Psychiatry have been issued since 1950; most of the current practices are described in these publications and they contain an extensive bibliography.[13] The First International Conference on Student Mental Health (held in 1956) resulted in a general survey of the field from an international point of view and a comprehensive series of recommendations designed to aid in preventing or minimizing emotional disorders among students.[14] Prior to this conference an extensive bibliographical volume was published for the use of its delegates.[15]

Psychiatric services, usually (and preferably) developed as part of college health services, are not competitors of the already well-established counseling programs but rather are collaborators with them in helping students to be able to learn. Such services have emphasized the need for special attention to the more severely disturbed students. As a result, college psychiatrists have learned much from the emotionally handicapped students which they believe can be used as the basis for a program to lessen such disability. As they plan preventive measures, they often find themselves in seeming competition with their colleagues who are professional counselors but not psychiatrists. Competition usually develops when there is little or no communication between the psychiatric service and the other groups. This deficiency may be due to lack of appreciation of the value of working together or it may be due to antipathy between one or more members of each group. Competition may also be encouraged when students have a choice as to which service they may select for help, especially when there is no opportunity for subsequent transfer to the service best suited to his needs. Gradually, however, the two types of counselors are learning to work together to the advantage of both, realizing that there is far more to be done than all counseling groups can possibly do.

The general principle that college psychiatric services should maintain effective collaboration with all other counseling agencies in their own institutions seems now to enjoy widespread acceptance and, in most universities, to be reflected in practice. Counseling groups agree that licensed physicians (psychiatrists, when they are available) have unique legal responsibility for patients who may harm themselves or others. Therefore, in doubtful situations involving suicide or homicide, or the development of a psychosis, a college psychiatric staff may be of great help to other counselors, safeguarding and strengthening their positions by appropriate consultation regarding any illness about which legal action may be necessary. Of course, if drug or shock therapy is needed, only physicians may prescribe such procedures. In many instances, the basic distinction must be made by a physician as to whether a given set of symptoms is due to physical or emotional causes.

Counselors who are not psychiatrists are of unique importance in testing, career guidance, help with study problems, and in carrying on psychotherapy (under supervision by a psychiatrist or with "genuine medical collaboration")* for the many students who are not critically ill.

There is considerable confusion as to what term to use in describing the function of the professor who aids students with personal problems which fall outside his usual role as consultant regarding course content. Some would use the term *advisor* to describe this function when performed by one without professional training. I prefer the term *counselor* for all who aid students in the task of integrating all their experiences into a coherent form. The teacher as counselor is interested not only

---

* See "McKeown Report," Final Report of the Committee to Study the Relationships of Medicine with Allied Health Professions and Services to the House of Delegates of the American Medical Association. Adopted June 16, 1960, 535 N. Dearborn St., Chicago, Illinois.

in how or whether the student acquires information but in what he does with it and how he uses it for his further development. If the teacher is a sensitive and empathetic human being, there will be students who will want to talk with him about personal concerns and, while they may be unrelated to specific course work, they are relevant to his general emotional development.

Counseling is one of the most important aids in improving relations between students and faculty. The functions of a counselor, appropriate approaches to counseling, and principles to be followed will be described. Suggestions for the improvement or establishment of a counseling system and in-service training for participants will follow.

To the counselor belongs the privilege and responsibility of helping to effectively disseminate useful knowledge and to encourage the development of young men and women of competence and integrity. The best teaching is of no avail if the student will not or cannot learn. Many causes underlie failure to learn in the presence of suitable opportunity; feelings and emotions figure very prominently among them. Whereas a teacher's basic desire is to impart subject matter skillfully, a counselor focuses his efforts on increasing the capacity and desire of a student to learn. Ideally, a good teacher is also interested in the latter.

A counselor may be a specially trained person who spends his entire time in conference with students. Or, he may be a teacher who believes that there is more to education than mastery of factual details and who is willing to support this view by taking a personal interest in his students' growth and development.

Whichever of these two views of a counselor's activities one may favor (and I happen to think that most counseling should be done by classroom teachers), competence is vital. A faculty member can be a specialist in his chosen discipline and at the same time be well acquainted with the personality characteristics of the age group with which he deals. Most teachers should have this bifocal point of view but, of course, some cannot acquire the latter for a variety of reasons.

There are three general approaches to counseling. The first

consists of the counselor's telling students what they should do and how to solve their problems. The reasoning proceeds that the counselor has lived longer than his students, has had more experience, has read more widely, and should be able to guide them wisely through the quandaries which they encounter daily. Isn't he getting paid because of his experience and wisdom? Why the nonsense of "beating about the bush" when proper courses of action are evident and can readily be pointed out by the counselor?

A second approach consists in such skillful manipulation of the students or their environment that they think they are doing what they want to do, but actually carry out the wishes of the counselor or parents. Of course, they may be quite dependent upon a very few people for their cues, but that is not serious— they will find others in later life whose actions they can use as models for their own. Someone will always appear to guide them in what they can and cannot do or think. Such counselors work behind the scenes, making clever changes here and there, manipulating the environment in subtle ways without the students' knowledge, thus unwittingly leaving their students poorly equipped to deal with the more powerful but still subtle manipulators of public opinion in national and international affairs. Altering the students' environment with his knowledge and cooperation is quite another matter, and often is quite helpful.

Finally, there is the philosophy of counseling based on the power of rational authority. Counselors discuss academic and personal problems openly, freely, and honestly. Confidences are respected and permission is obtained for discussion of personal matters with other interested individuals. New points of view are brought to students' attention without pressure to adopt any one of them. Opinions are expressed, but advice is given sparingly and not imposed on students. The possible results of decisions are pointed out. The emphasis is on what is desirable for students and all those who are concerned with their welfare—on *what* is right rather than *who* is right.

Students need and appreciate counseling by older colleagues whom they respect, because so often their problems are based on factors outside their usual experiences. They are often reacting to new stresses which reactivate old unresolved problems. The more experienced counselor can help the student make sense to himself by careful listening, pointing out possibilities not previously entertained, and asking searching questions.

Relations between students and faculty members could be much improved in most colleges. Most students do not appreciate being treated impersonally, as if they were "numbers in a computer or holes in an IBM card." Many influences operate to prevent friendly and natural contacts between students and teachers outside the classroom. Students may hesitate to seek out such contacts because their actions may be interpreted by their peers or teachers as seeking special favors. Faculty members are often ill at ease with students ("What do you say when you are alone in a room with a student?") or they may fear becoming involved in an emotional problem with which a student is struggling. Some may feel apprehensive about making students dependent upon them. Others consider time spent informally with students as wasted. The heavy schedules required of many teachers leave little time for personal contact even for those who wish to be on friendly personal terms with their students.

Faculty members who fail to take the questions of their students seriously do them a grave injustice. A young person so let down will develop a self-depreciatory attitude about himself. The dean who says, "Are you going to be my problem child this year?" reveals his own shortcomings and shows that he fails to respect the student.

Good relations between students and faculty members are supposedly more prevalent in small colleges than in the large universities. At least they are praised more often in the catalogues of the former. Like health and money, they are best appreciated when they are deficient or absent. The complaints of disaffected students often include the allegation that faculty members do not have time for them, not only because the student-faculty ratio is increasing but because of emphasis on research to the detriment of teaching. Even if students do not wish to have personal contact with their teachers, they like to think of them as being available when needed.

There is no absolute reason why relations between students and faculty members in large institutions cannot be as cordial and stimulating as those in the smaller colleges. In practice, however, the impediments are numerous. The basic attitudes of an individual change perceptibly when he goes from a small town to a large city; there is a similar change in the expectations of both students and teachers when they go from a small institution to a larger one. Impersonality is almost taken for granted. Since one cannot know everyone, little effort may be taken to become acquainted with as many people as one would know almost automatically in a small college. To overcome the tendencies toward anonymity and impersonality in a large university requires much thought and effort on the part of many faculty members, not just those whose primary responsibility is counseling.

In the effort to improve faculty student relations, great care must be taken to see that students do not feel that their privacy is being violated. Some students do not want "interference" by others. They prefer to work alone, or in highly idiosyncratic ways. These preferences should be respected. Attention should not be forced upon anyone unless his behavior is so deviant as to be disruptive of the lives of others or clearly damaging to himself. When the latter situations occur, the individual is usually emotionally or mentally ill.

A counselor should be cautious in getting information from a troubled student, both in the questions he asks him and in how much he permits a student to say about himself while obviously under intense emotional strain. When a student begins to divulge intimate personal details of thoughts or behavior which are more appropriate for the ears of a professional counselor, the teacher-counselor might well suggest that he see such a person, if available, or conclude the interview as quickly as he can tactfully do so, suggesting that he come back the next day for a few minutes. By that time, the student who is telling too much about himself in an unguarded way may have a chance to organize his defenses and may possibly use better judgment than he previously exercised. The student who exposes his inner thoughts and feelings to a teacher in this way may feel awkward in subsequent relations with the teacher and avoid him because of embarrassment. Excessive encouragement of confidences or of introspection, appropriately called aggressive intervention, should be avoided by teacher-counselors and professionals alike. A troubled student should be allowed to say what is on his mind in his own way and at his own rate, unless, as suggested above, he becomes involved in a cycle in which each disclosure stimulates others even more private.

Counselors must be careful to avoid adopting distorted views of parents as a result of disclosures to them from their students. As college students discuss their problems, it soon becomes obvious that many of them are unhappy about parental discord, parental domination, or other aspects of parents' behavior. It should be remembered that when young people describe the current strong feelings they have toward their parents, these do not necessarily reflect their more enduring feelings or even the preponderance of their sentiments at the time. It is easy to become too critical of parents when only one side of a story is heard.

Many of our students have little opportunity to have conversations with their older respected colleagues on the faculty about personal or academic matters. When such opportunities do occur, there is no compelling reason why discussion should be limited to matters of direct concern in the classroom. One of my colleagues who is highly respected by all his students discussed this point in a seminar; he said he saw no reason why a student who came to his instructor with several questions should not have appropriate attention given to each, even if some of them involved personal quandaries. He believed that many problems might be resolved in this manner if teachers listened attentively and patiently, whereas without such attention more of them would ultimately require professional attention for their resolution.

In his counseling role, a teacher should be as concerned with how his students feel about their work as with their competence, since if their attitudes are poor their proficiency is not likely to be increased rapidly. If they can be helped to enjoy their work, to appreciate what it means to them, and to acquire a sense of competence in what they are doing, they are in a good position to solve many of their developmental tasks, rather than having them become magnified until serious psychopathology results.

Conversations with students in a counseling situation may be a source of anxiety to teachers because they are too eager to do something tangible for them. The tendency to try to do too much for a student in distress must be held in check. It may seem easier to tell a disturbed student who comes for help what he should do than to take the time to learn enough about him to help him make an intelligent choice of his own. If such a student is given direct advice, he is deprived of the satisfaction of having made the decision if it happens to be a good one; he has a convenient scapegoat (the teacher) if the decision was a poor one. In either case maturation is not furthered. Teachers must realize that they cannot help every student who comes to them for advice in a direct or specific way. Quite often the best that can be done is to listen with care and sympathy in an attempt to understand, and possibly ask an appropriate question or seek some clarification of an issue when appropriate. By this process, students can be aided in understanding themselves better. The good results of counseling, like that of other forms of teaching, may not become apparent for a long time.

All teachers should learn how to make appropriate referrals. Many teachers do not know what counseling facilities are available in their own institutions. This knowledge may not be easy to acquire, particularly if the various counseling agencies are uncoordinated and have no common spokesman. In the small colleges, most referrals are to the office of the dean of Students, with a few to the Health Service. In the larger universities, there may be a bewildering variety of resources, often scattered in different departments. The diversity and geographical dispersion may be quite advantageous, provided that coordination is such that every student in need of help is referred to the agency best suited to deal with his problem.

The college psychiatrist should be freely available to faculty members for consultation whenever the latter have students whose behavior does not make sense to them. Referral is almost always indicated when a student is preoccupied with thoughts of suicide or homicide, has been involved in overt homosexual activities, exhibitionism, or other socially unacceptable sexual behavior, or is unduly agitated without obvious precipitating cause. There are many borderline situations, however, in which a preliminary conference between the teacher and the psychiatrist will serve to determine appropriate action. In the early stages of a counseling program, before the role of college psychiatrists is well understood, some teachers may see the suggestion that they discuss or make referrals as a reflection on their ability. When they learn that such consultations and appropriate referrals are a sign of strength and not weakness, the resistance nearly always disappears. The tact displayed by the consulting psychiatrist is a crucial factor in encouraging such cooperation.

If counselors are to work comfortably with their students, they should have support from some of their colleagues in the psychological sciences. The more complete and adequate the counseling program is in a given institution, the more danger that faculty members will tend to refer all problems to one of its division, thus furthering the idea that academic and emotional maturation are separate considerations. If there are no professional counselors, the danger arises that a teacher may feel it necessary to keep on working with a disturbed student long after he should be in the care of a psychiatrist or a mental health clinic. One of the most important duties of a counselor is to recognize when a serious problem exists.

In the smaller colleges, in which only a small portion of professional counselors' time is available, it is desirable that that time be spent, in part at least, in consultation with teachers who are concerned about particular students and who wonder whether their behavior is within reasonable or expected limits or whether it calls for referral to someone with greater skills—a clinical psychologist, a social worker, or a psychiatrist. When teachers and professional counselors work together in this way each group becomes more aware of the work of the other and the effectiveness of each is increased. This is one of the best methods by which knowledge of the psychology of young adults is furthered throughout the institution.

As the pressure on our young people in the secondary schools to go to college increases, and as scholarships and loans become more available, our colleges will admit many students whose values and backgrounds are quite different from those of most of our present college students. Inevitably, this will produce much uneasiness on the part of those students who suddenly find themselves in an environment in which any or all of their beliefs may be challenged. Not only will there be a need for skillful counseling by teachers, but juniors and seniors should be enlisted to aid these students in their transition to a more complex society. Their task will be to help those students to feel at home in the intellectual atmosphere which is new and strange to them, and to assure them that the process takes time, hoping thereby to avoid hasty or impulsive attempts to end the anxiety created by the adjustment to the new style of living. An upperclassman counselor, who has the benefit of some supervision by a more experienced (preferably professional) counselor, can often help a naive freshman better than an older person, particularly if he himself has recently successfully accomplished a similar adaptation.

An upperclassman who acts as counselor to freshmen may need help from a faculty member with wider experience in counseling. Accordingly, some colleges develop teams of counselors, with the upperclassman being responsible for perhaps eight to ten freshmen while the faculty member exercises general oversight of two such groups.[16]

No single method or system of counseling will serve the needs of all institutions. Neither is it desirable to adopt some particular scheme of describing personality and give it a semi-official status. New and helpful ideas designed to improve students' attitudes toward acquiring intellectual facility come from many sources. Memorizing a system or philosophy developed by a research worker, no matter how good it may be in its original context, can easily lead to ready and facile verbalization by a counselor without a true understanding of the emotional dynamics of students. Rogers has made major contributions to the theory and practice of counseling. Erikson's work has become so well accepted that he has had to caution against the uncritical application of his views to all situations. Freud's basic concepts underlie all explanations of human behavior to some extent, even those formulated by those who proudly boast of their hostility to them. The ideas of these and many other students in the field can all contribute to an increased understanding of the psychology of the young adult and ways of helping him to harness his own energies constructively. No theory of personality development or system of counseling has yet been developed that is suitable for all circumstances.

The psychological sophistication of college students varies among colleges according to the psychological influences to which they have been exposed. The enormous publicity given to mental health promotional measures has apparently had some effect on the level of knowledge concerning mental disorders in some communities.[17] There is reason to think that college students have changed even more than the general population in their attitudes toward and knowledge of factors influencing mental health. Most college psychiatrists believe that students are in general more receptive to psychological explanations of their problems than either their parents or faculty members. A prudent attitude for a faculty member to adopt is that the general level of receptivity to psychological analysis of personal problems is greater among students than among his own colleagues. Of course some students look at their problems in so intellectual a manner that they are able to use their technical knowledge to avoid understanding the more subtle feelings derived from unconscious sources.

Several principles may profitably be kept in mind by those who are responsible for establishing or improving counseling in college. First, aggressive efforts to get a program started may result in its becoming the target of criticism from those who believe the old ways are always good enough, or even more regrettably may lead others to expect more from the program than it can be expected to achieve. Progress should be made with as little fanfare as possible. If a counseling plan is to work at all, it must have the active support of the faculty and the respect of students. No matter how good a system may look on paper it cannot survive faculty and student indifference. The ideal program should be based on a widespread awareness on the parts of teachers, administrators, trustees, and parents as to what the need for it is, what problems it is designed to solve, and what elements of flexibility are inherent in it to permit its adaptation to continually changing conditions. Attainment of this goal usually calls for much discussion by many individuals and groups, aided by a few persons who have had considerable experience in the practical as well as the theoretical aspects of counseling. If a college counseling program has the services of a psychologist or psychiatrist only a few hours a week, most of his time should be spent in conferences with counselors rather than with students. The time and ability of those who are most highly skilled should be used, insofar as possible, in raising the general level of the counselors' abilities.

Proponents of counseling should also avoid oversimplification or overselling. Far more is involved than securing teachers willing to counsel and assigning students to them. Although the program should be relatively inconspicuous, its presence implies that a considerable number of faculty members are as much concerned with how their students react to their school experiences as with imparting subject matter. Interest in the attitudes of students toward learning is a desirable means of ultimately influencing them to learn more than they would have otherwise.

An essential early step in the development or radical reorganization of a counseling program in college is creation of an awareness on the parts of faculty members, administrators, and governing boards of the nature of the problems it is designed to explore. Even student leaders should be invited to many of the discussions, since much can be learned from the consumer's point of view. Counseling is not the answer to all the problems of education, but is merely one of the devices designed to keep the whole educational process from becoming impersonal and to keep attention focused on the needs and responsibilities of the individual. It is an attempt to do for all students what good teachers have always been able to accomplish for some students.

The next step which is most helpful in the continuance and elaboration of a good program is the selection of a resource person—a teacher already well-liked and respected, and recognized as capable in a particular discipline, to acquaint himself thoroughly with the principles, philosophy, and techniques of counseling. Competence in the field of counseling is the key requisite for such a person, and opinions differ as to how it can be obtained. I do not believe that most counselors should be full-time. I believe they should be trained initially in one of the basic academic disciplines and maintain their professional activity and at least some teaching in that field. For many such part-time counselors psychology may be the basic discipline, particularly those who are to be the resource persons I am now describing. More counseling should be done by all teachers, particularly as they acquire increasing facility and ease in such activities. When they encounter unusual problems with their students they may consult the special resource person (or director of counseling) rather than referring them immediately to a specialist.

A very desirable by-product of a counseling program is the accumulation of a considerable number of faculty members who have been involved in its more formal aspects but who have become "alumni" of the system, so to speak, and who retain their interest in aiding students in the resolution of their quandaries long after they have been involved in a structural system. They have been said to have developed the "counseling attitude."[18] Many students will go to these informal counselors whom they have learned to trust who will not go to a counselor who has been assigned to them.

Some teachers may be excellent in imparting subject matter but very poor in counseling. They may be ill at ease with students, hostile to them, or lacking in understanding of the social changes which have occurred since they were of college age. Some of them may not have worked out their own personal problems sufficiently to permit them to act maturely in all spheres. Their points of view should be respected and they should not be forced into counseling activities against their wishes. Those who think they are good counselors but are not should be dissuaded from participation in as diplomatic a manner as possible.

Following the creation of a general understanding of the purposes of a counseling system and the selection of the resource person (or specialist) in counseling, a continuous in-service training program for faculty members should be instituted. The content of such a program is still a highly debatable matter, but its essential focus is on the reasons for the behavior exhibited by students. Those who are apparently very successful in their work deserve attention no less, and possibly more, than those who are coping with apparent difficulties. The components of the normal personality and the effects on it of adverse conditions during early life are fundamental considerations for any teacher interested in counseling.

It has long been known that knowledge about the emotional aspects of maturation, or of the emotional components of disease, can be acquired most readily when the teacher (or physician in medical situations) works with psychiatrists on cases with which they are immediately or intimately concerned. Lectures on theories of personality or human development do little good; teachers' interest can seldom be aroused through such didactic procedures. Teachers, like their students, learn best when the subject matter has meaning for them at the time the discussions are held. Theoretical knowledge may be a prelude to learning but is usually quite inadequate in isolation. It is best acquired while working with psychiatrists, psychologists, or social workers on issues of mutual concern.

A Counseling Institute for secondary school teachers and headmasters organized along the lines suggested above has been particularly successful. Under the auspices of the Harvard University Health Services and the Northfield and Mount Hermon Schools of Northfield, Massachusetts, five psychiatrists and psychologists from the Harvard Health Services, experienced in the type of counseling expounded in this book, and about sixty faculty members of secondaries (2 to 3 from each school) meet together on the campus of the Northfield School for eight days of intensive discussions. The Institute is designed to cover three major topics: (1) the student in his home and school environment and the kinds of problems presented there; (2) effective counseling procedures which can be utilized by faculty members, and (3) signs of more serious disorder and the use of a referral system for professional help. The program consists of lectures, small group discussions (12 persons), and panel discussions by the faculty. Group discussions follow each lecture; a psychiatrist or psychologist moderates each one. Case materials prepared by participants from the secondary schools provide foci for intense analysis of pertinent issues. The lectures are both general (The Milieu for Counseling, Counseling Procedures, The Counselor and His Feelings, Common Problems in Counseling, and "Red Flags" or Danger Signs) and specific (Stealing, Homosexuality, Problems in College Admission, Sexual Education, Discipline, Cultural Deprivation, Minority Groups and Their Problems, etc.).

The aims of the Institute are three-fold:

(1) To help the counselor understand the limits of his skills and to recognize the signs of more serious disorders in the students he counsels. To help the counselor utilize an effective referral system so that the student may receive optimum help.

(2) To help the counselor view student problems in terms of the factors which cause them, looking at the school, the home, and the development of the individual. To help the counselor understand his own school in terms of factors that can hinder or help the student in solving problems. To help the counselor see the way in which strong feelings grow out of situations which have taken place in the past.

(3) To help the counselor understand the nature of the emotional relationship with a student in a counseling situation and learn how to use the feelings in an effective way. To help the counselor become aware of factors in himself that can impede the counseling situation. To help the counselor clarify to himself the goals he hopes to achieve with the student. To help the counselor learn techniques that will encourage the student to express his feelings, reassess his actions, and make realistic decisions.

Judging from the comments of those who have attended these institutes, as well as from the headmasters of their schools, their purposes have been accomplished. A particularly promising feature is that some schools have had delegations in successive years, and the separate groups have met in their own schools to devise ways of improving counseling efficiency in the rest of the faculty as well as continuing to further their own knowledge and skills.

What is unusual about this project is the fact that it was accomplished at all. The pedagogical theories were not new. The issues at stake have long been a source of concern to all teachers and counselors. Most importantly, a private foundation supported the project, recognizing what has been known all along, that we have much more knowledge about the emotional aspects of learning than is being used. Research in how to use the knowledge we have is more urgently needed than acquiring new theoretical knowledge to lie unused. This is an example that could be followed by college faculty members and administrators if support were made available.

Obviously, there are many ways of describing the course of development from birth to maturity. Any comprehensive account of personality formation should take into full consideration biological, psychological, and social factors (see Chapter III). The period of greatest interest to college counselors, the time when the boy or girl is struggling to determine who and what he is, what he wants to become, what his concept of himself may be, and how to resolve a whole series of development crises, is well summarized in a recent publication resulting from the First International Conference on Student Mental Health.[19]

From the educator's point of view, the development of integrity is fully as important, if not more so, than acquisition of intellectual facility. This cannot be taught without the presence, among faculty members and other significant persons in the community, of models for identification who can be and are respected by students. Hence, in an in-service training program counselors must of necessity give considerable attention to understanding themselves. Their influence when off-guard and acting naturally is more powerful and pervasive than their official utterances in the classroom.

In any case, a counselor should continually keep himself informed of the customs, peer-group pressures and the social or cultural characteristics of the students in his school. He should remember that the lives for which his students are preparing will be vastly different from his own and that no one can now foresee what their main features may be. The topics of greatest interest will vary from year to year.

These issues suggest that counseling consists of much more than telling students what they should do or giving them information. Paternalism has no place in such activity. Even the term "guidance" calls for clarification. If the tacit assumption is made that the counselor's duty is to guide his students into the right path, grave errors may result. Who defines the "right" path? And who sees that he takes it? The counselor's job is to help the students to make their own decisions, suggest new points of view for consideration, even support their right to make decisions which the counselor deems unwise, so long as they do not violate the recognized laws and customs of the community.

A statement made by Professor Philip Jacob about college students is pertinent:

> "College can contribute to the growth of a student's values only when it penetrates the core of his life and confronts him with fresh and often disturbing implications, which are different from those which he and his society have taken for granted. This can hardly occur as a by-product of a curricular assembly line. It requires a highly personal relationship between the college community and the individual student—a relationship that is warm and considerate, but at the same time mutually aggravating."[20]

The individual counselor should keep in mind the limitations and potential difficulties which are all too common in counseling relationships. Counseling cannot solve all problems; for many of them there are no satisfactory solutions. Counseling is desirable because it permits open-ended communication between teachers and students and focuses attention on students' emotional reactions to their formal educational experiences. These two aspects of education, student-teacher interchange and emotional responses to education, are often grossly neglected.

The delicate issues surrounding the question of confidentiality in the counseling relationship are still difficult to resolve and in many instances unclear. The policies usually followed in the relations between psychiatrists and students have been discussed elsewhere.[21] How completely these can be superimposed upon the relation between a nonprofessional counselor and a student is an open question which should be discussed often and at length in each school or college. In any case, no student should ever be led to divulge highly personal and private, possibly incriminating, information to a counselor, believing that he is in a confidential relationship to him, only to have the counselor relay the information to the dean. A counselor who believes that he must report every questionable thought or behavior to those in authority has failed to understand his true function. Conversely, a counselor who will never report anything, no matter how antisocial or ominous, may be a party to tragic consequences.

Counseling and discipline ought to be kept separate to the greatest possible extent. Students should have someone to whom they can turn when troubled who is not obliged to report to the dean if disciplinary situations are discussed. If the chief administrator simply must know everything students confide in their counselors, a good counseling program is impossible. A president or dean will have to trust his counselor-teachers to handle delicate material constructively without breaking students' confidences, else he prevents many students from getting help they sorely need. When a student comes to a counselor and divulges information about himself which, if known, would result in disciplinary action, there is no great cause for worry; the student is already concerned about his behavior and the ideal teaching situation is present to aid him in developing more responsible patterns of behavior.

Moralizing and reminiscing should be kept at a minimum. I have known of students returning from interviews filled with moralizing, fully convinced that the counselors had no real awareness of their problems. Another one said of his counselor, "I really didn't get very much from him because he talked about his own problems so much that there was no time for him to hear about mine."

In a very real sense, the in-service training of a counselor bears many resemblances to the training of his student. In both instances, guide lines are often absent or indistinct. Decisions often must be made "on the basis of insufficient and constantly changing facts." Respect for students and subject matter is necessary for best results. A continual desire to learn more is the most reliable sign of a successful educational experience. Permeating both the activities of counselor and students is a concern for quality, feeling, sensitiveness, and capacity to respond to new situations appropriately. "Culture is activity of thought, and receptiveness to beauty and humane feeling. Scraps of information have nothing to do with it." I feel sure that Whitehead, in making this statement in his *Aims of Education,* did not mean to underestimate the need for accurate information, but to emphasize that something more is needed. Counseling is primarily concerned with that "something more."

We are hearing and will continue to hear much about the irresponsibility of college students. They cannot rise above the level of behavior they observe about them unless stimulated to do so by teachers or parents whom they respect and love. They need limits and guide lines, imposed with firmness, friendliness, and respect. The values they assimilate can be better than those now motivating most people in their home communities. Values cannot be chosen for them—they must adopt them for themselves. They need discussion of the issues involved in making decisions regarding their own future rather than having another person's answers given to them. Counseling is one of the effective ways of bringing these issues to their attention while at the same time providing a stimulus and opportunity for their exploration. In all our efforts to improve counseling, we will always have to be on guard to prevent the process from becoming mechanical, routine, systematized, taken for granted, and ultimately useless. As in other aspects of education, "the letter killeth but the spirit giveth life."

REFERENCES

1. ARBUCKLE, D. S.: *Counseling: An Introduction.* Boston, Allyn and Bacon, 1961.
2. BORDIN, E. S.: *Psychological Counseling.* New York, Appleton, 1955.
3. ROGERS, C. B.: *Counseling and Psychotherapy.* Boston, Houghton, 1942.

4. ————————: *Client Centered Therapy.* Boston, Houghton, 1951.

5. ————————: *On Becoming a Person.* Boston, Houghton, 1961.

6. SUPER, D. E.: *The Psychology of Careers.* New York, Harper, 1957.

7. TYLER, L. E.: *The Work of the Counselor.* Rev. Ed. New York, Appleton, 1961.

8. WILLIAMSON, E. G.: *Student Personnel Services in Colleges and Universities.* New York, McGraw-Hill, 1953.

9. ————————: *Vocational Counseling.* New York, McGraw-Hill, 1965.

10. FRY, C. C.: *Mental Health in College.* New York. Commonwealth Fund, 1942.

11. FARNSWORTH, D. L.: *Mental Health in College and University.* Cambridge, Harvard, 1957.

12. WEDGE, B. M., Ed.: *Psychosocial Problems of College Men.* New Haven, Yale, 1958.

13. Group for the Advancement of Psychiatry: *The Role of Psychiatrists in Colleges and Universities.* GAP Report No. 17, revised January 1957.

13a. ————————: *Considerations on Personality Development in College Students.* GAP Report No. 32, May 1955.

13b. ————————: *The College Experience*: *A Focus for Psychiatric Research.* GAP Report No. 52, May 1962.

14. FUNKENSTEIN, D. H., Ed.: *The Student and Mental Health—An International View.* New York, World Federation for Mental Health, 1959. (This volume is obtainable only from the World Federation for Mental Health, 124 E. 28th St., New York, N. Y.)

15. FUNKENSTEIN, D. H., AND WILKIE, G. H.: *Student Mental Health*: *An Annotated Bibliography 1936-55.* New York, World Federation for Mental Health and International Association of Universities, 1956.

16. FARNSWORTH, D. L.: Maturity through student counseling. *Phi Delta Kappa,* February 1955, p. 185.

17. LEMKAU, P. V., AND CROCETTI, A. M.: An urban population's opinion and knowledge about mental illness. *Amer. J. Psychiat., 118*:692-700, 1962.

18. FARNSWORTH, D. L.: *Mental Health in College and University.* Cambridge, Harvard, 1957, p. 115.

19. ERIKSON, E. H.: Late adolescence. In: *The Student and Mental Health—An International View*, D. H. Funkenstein, Ed. New York, World Federation for Mental Health, 1959, pp. 66-106.

20. JACOB, P.: In: *Spotlight on the College Student*, M. Habein, Ed. Washington, Amer. Council Education, 1959, p. 5.

21. FARNSWORTH, D. L., Ed.: *College Health Administration*. New York, Appleton, 1964, pp. 72-78.

CHAPTER XI

CONFIDENTIALITY AND PRIVILEGED
COMMUNICATION

W ITH THE INCREASED attention now being paid to students' "rights" in all areas of college life it is only logical that the problem of confidentiality should be frequently discussed. College physicians, and particularly psychiatrists, have constantly been attempting to develop rules and customs regarding the safeguarding of the confidences of their patients, but many uncertainties and complexities remain. If primary emphasis is always placed on adhering to the letter of rules of confidentiality, students may suffer grave injustices—for example, help urgently needed might have been available had one college official informed certain others of the possible need for it in the case of a particular student. On the other hand, if all those participating in counseling have available to them the records of all others in the college who engage in counseling, it becomes quite probable that breaks in confidence will occur that may do serious harm to a student. Fortunately, the need for confidentiality and the subtleties of maintaining it are becoming nearly as well appreciated among faculty members generally as among those with the professional responsibilities of the usual psychiatric team (psychiatrist, psychologist, and psychiatric social worker).

The rules of confidentiality observed by psychiatrists and other professional counselors are either identical or so similar that exchange of confidential information among psychiatrists and other counselors should be on the same basis as that among psychiatrists alone. This is particularly true in groups that have become accustomed to working together and who trust one another implicitly. Obviously many problems remain: when does a person become a counselor? The boundary is not as distinct as it is in the case of psychiatrists. Should students in training for guidance and counseling careers be granted access to confidential records?

Indoctrination in the necessity and procedures of confidentiality should be conducted at the beginning of training programs for student counselors. Such students should not have access to records of other students. Records of highly intimate material should be as devoid of detail as possible. Extreme care should be taken by the recorder to see that the necessary information is conveyed, omitting delicate information which may be harmful but not necessary. For example, a student may be promiscuous and troubled about her lack of impulse control. It would be neither desirable nor necessary to go into detail as to persons, places, and methods involved. Records should be dignified as well as accurate and restrained.

Confidentiality is defined by the Committee on Psychiatry and the Law of the Group for the Advancement of Psychiatry as the relationship between a physician (psychiatrist) and his patient, in which the patient may assume that his disclosures will not be passed on to others except under certain circumstances, and then only for the specific purpose of lending necessary help. This takes place within the framework of the social and professional roles of the physician as one who treats and helps his patients and who is ethically committed to this role.

The legal aspects of confidentiality are based on the individual's right of privacy. It includes the contractual right of the patient, expressed or implied, that the psychiatrist shall refrain from violating his obligation to maintain the confidential relationship. The patient has a right of privacy, and, if the psychiatrist violates that right by making private information public, he becomes liable, in many states, for damages in a tort action.

Privileged communication is a right existing only by statute whereby a patient may bar his physician from testifying about his medical treatment and from disclosing information about it. Approximately two-thirds of the states or other jurisdictions in the United States have such statutes. When such privilege exists, it is a legal right which belongs to the patient and not to the physician. Many psychiatrists do not realize that in the jurisdiction in which they practice their patients may not possess the right of privilege. Some do not appreciate that their patients' assumption of confidentiality imposes a legal obligation upon them.* When disclosures of a private nature are made, the written permission of the patient (client, advisee, etc.) is necessary.

Cass and Curran point out that the right of privilege is part of a patient's right of privacy, a right which is based on the theory that the details of a person's life are private and sacred from intrusion.[1] The legal protection of this right is a relatively new legal phenomenon. These authors predict that there will be a great surge forward in the enforcement of "privacy right" in the near future as a result of a 1965 U. S. Supreme Court decision which recognized the right of privacy as a fundamental human right guaranteed by the Bill of Rights.[2]

Sometimes a parent objects because his son or daughter has been allowed to consult a psychiatrist without his permission. A suit against the college may be threatened. Assuming that all other aspects of confidentiality have been appropriately managed (as described in this chapter), this type of objection can be dealt with successfully. It is not advisable or necessary for a college psychiatrist to report whom he sees to parents or the administration, unless there are overriding considerations (to be described below). In fact, it is a breach of confidence for him to do so without his patient's permission, or in the case of certain other situations, his knowledge.

If a college psychiatrist were to report students' consultations to all parents, or if he were to require permission from them for a consultation, his usefulness would cease. Students simply would not come to see him. They would, therefore, be deprived of a service which might be quite essential for them. The

---

* An excellent discussion of the problems of confidentiality and privileged communication is contained in Group for the Advancement of Psychiatry Report No. 45, *Confidentiality and Privileged Communication in the Practice of Psychiatry*, June 1960, Publication Office—104 East 25th Street, New York.

psychiatrist is a member of the staff of the college. Any student should be able to consult him with the same freedom as he would consult with a teacher outside the classroom. Similarly, he is free to consult a physician or nurse at the health center or infirmary. The college psychiatrist is a physician and should be considered in the same general category as any of the other medical specialists.

If a student is genuinely suicidal, psychotic, or involved in situations which will soon become known in the community and which will reflect adversely on his parents, the usual rules of confidence would be superseded. The parents should be notified, but the student should be informed of the notification and the reasons for it. This situation is analogous to that of the surgeon who sees any student without permission; if a serious operation is to be performed, permission must be obtained.

An awkward and frustrating situation sometimes arises when parents, fellow students, or faculty members become uneasy about the emotional status of a student, yet do not want him to know of their concern. A delegation of one or more of them may secure an appointment with the college psychiatrist, acquaint him with their observations and fears, but refuse permission for him to try to help the alleged patient on the basis of their report. This of course puts the psychiatrist, representing the college health service, in a delicate position. If he does nothing, and the student takes destructive action, he may feel partly responsible for the tragedy. If he breaks confidence and makes a contact with the supposed patient, he may incur the displeasure of both the informers and the individual about whom they were reporting. In such a situation the college psychiatrist can only remain silent, but he should make a full record of all that transpired, noting the refusal to give permission to act on the basis of evidence submitted.

However, the situation cannot always be handled so simply. The individual about whom concern is expressed may be homicidal and making active preparations to carry out his designs. Such an emergency would require efforts on his behalf by everyone who had some responsibility for the disturbed person. Consultations would be in order (with very strict precautions about secrecy in the event the fears were unfounded) involving the psychiatrist, student health director, the dean of students, the senior officer in charge of the dormitory or fraternity, the president (in a small college), and possibly the parents or other relatives. Usually the chief of the campus police force is kept informed from the beginning. All this could be done without placing the original informants in special jeopardy because they had tried to act in the best interests of the student and others in the institution. The basic responsibility would have to be shared by the health service and the dean's office prior to the establishment of the truth or falsity of the original reports. Once a diagnosis of mental illness is made, the basic responsibility falls upon the psychiatrist or head of the health service.

When the dean or another administrative official seeks a consultation with the college psychiatrist for a student who allegedly has been breaking the law or committing a serious infraction of college regulations (stealing, cheating, overt homosexual activity, etc.), a modification of the usual rules of confidentiality is necessary. The student should be informed that the interview is being conducted to help him as well as the college disciplinary officials, but that a report must be made to the referring official and that he will be informed as to the nature of its contents. With this forewarning, the student is then free (1) to give no information; (2) to tell the psychiatrist only what he thinks will be in his best interest, or (3) to make a full and frank admission of all his activities. He should also be told that when the point at issue has been settled and the penalty, if any, has been determined, he may return for help if he so desires and the interviews will then be completely confidential.

If a student does not cooperate with the psychiatrist, which is his privilege, the disciplinary procedures will be carried out with the assumption that he is fully responsible for his acts. If, however, the student refuses to cooperate and his behavior is obviously that of a psychotic person, it would be the duty of the psychiatrist to report to the proper administrative official that the disposition of the case should be a medical rather than a purely administrative one. The student (or his next of kin) should be informed of the nature of the report as would be done if he were not ill.

In occasional instances, a dean of students may engage as a consultant a psychiatrist who reports directly to him, seeing students in his professional capacity, giving the impression that the interviews are confidential, and subsequently submitting a psychiatric record to the dean for his files. This constitutes a clear violation of medical ethics and should be condemned without reservation. Fortunately, such episodes are rare and should soon be nonexistent.

Some institutions ask for health information to be returned to the Admissions Committee headed by a lay person. However, it is inappropriate for medical information to be given to a lay person rather than to a physician; a more satisfactory solution should be worked out.

In most colleges with psychiatric services, faculty members who have no official counseling functions (other than those implied by being a teacher) occasionally refer a student to a psychiatrist for consultation and whatever subsequent treatment may be indicated. In this case, he will probably feel a considerable sense of responsibility and may wish to know whether the student has made and kept an appointment and whether or not it was justified. If he calls, or consults with, the psychiatrist, what should he be told? He can be told that the student did, or did not, make and keep the appointment. He can be told that the problem was a simple or a complex one, that his referral was appreciated, and informed of the attitude he might take with the student to make him as comfortable and relaxed as possible. The psychiatrist cannot give any personal information about the student, but he can listen to anything the faculty member, or anyone else, wishes to say to him. As added precautions in observing the student's privacy, he should indicate tactfully that conversations with a faculty member are themselves confidential, and he should ask permission of the student to talk with the faculty member who referred him if there is to be any additional communication beyond acknowledgment of the referral.

An ethical and usually desirable procedure for a college psychiatrist to pursue when information is being sought, after explaining the restrictions imposed by the need for confidence, is to explain what usually happens in similar situations, what kind of management is likely to be most helpful, and what the outcome is apt to be. In this manner, the student in question is protected while the person who wishes to help is given information which will enable him to understand the present situation and be in a better position to cooperate when other students show signs of emotional disturbance.

Although these rules for preserving privacy may seem obvious and hardly worth stating (to those who have long been aware of their necessity), an occasional teacher may become offended if information regarding a student whom he has referred for consultation is denied him. This is particularly true if the psychiatrist is tactless and says, "I'm sorry, I can't talk with anyone about a patient unless I have his written permission." Both the teacher and the psychiatrist may feel that their positions are correct, but each feels that the other has been lacking in consideration. The result is a lowering of the esteem in which the psychiatric service is held, because the teacher will usually (and understandably) share his annoyance and frustration with his colleagues.*

There is no reason why a psychiatrist may not receive communications from a parent regardless of whether or not the patient has given his permission, but he must indicate to them that it will be entirely one-sided: that is, communication of information from the parent to the psychiatrist. A full and frank discussion with the parent explaining the reasons for such confidentiality is desirable, even mandatory.

Furthermore, it is necessary to inform parents, particularly when the student is under twenty-one, whenever a patient is psychotic, or when there has been a suicidal attempt or strong

---

* Blaine's analysis of a number of the common situations involving confidentiality, ethics, and divided loyalty, with examples of how they may be resolved may be found in his article entitled Divided Loyalties: the College Therapist's Responsibility to the Student, the University and the Parents, *American Journal of Orthopsychiatry*, 34:481-485, April 1964.

suicidal preoccupation. Similarly, parents must be notified if there has been any lawbreaking and when it is necessary to require the student to leave school because of reasons either directly or indirectly related to emotional difficulties. Under most circumstances, permission from the student to break confidence is not difficult to obtain. The main point to emphasize is that the student patient should know the rules and reasons for his psychiatrist's actions so that he can understand what goes on around him; in other words, everyone should act honestly and consistently.

What is to be done about notifying administrative officials, roomates, or house mothers about a student who has made a suicidal gesture? If it is a serious one, key officials and parents should be informed. If it is a comparatively minor affair, it is entirely possible that more harm might be done the individual by notifying the administrators and parents than if this were not done. However, the problem is that of differentiating between a major suicidal gesture and a minor one. There is no set rule that can be established. For example: a student mentions the possibility of suicide as a manipulative gesture, but really does not intend to do it, and his half-hearted or feeble attempt comes to the attention of a physician, who in turn notifies someone who will later be involved in writing recommendations for graduate school; quite obviously this person's recommendation will be cast in different terms, because of his inside knowledge, than if he had not had that knowledge. In short, the student's privacy has been invaded. When a student has actually made a true suicidal gesture, he automatically relinquishes his rights to privacy. In some states a suicidal gesture is a criminal action, and the civil authorities are supposed to be notified. A physician has a right to notify the police, but few do because they know that unless the situation is a serious one, the difficulties begin to multiply as a result.

Administrative officers in colleges are frequently very unhappy when the health services—and particularly the psychiatric division—do not give them sufficient information about disturbed students, particularly those who have threatened suicide, to enable them to act intelligently when they are contacted by members of such a student's family. Information about students who have attempted suicide, threatened it, or talked about it frequently reaches house masters and deans through other channels, and they feel the psychiatrist has been unfair in not warning them (of course confidentially). Perhaps it is wise for all who deal with the more intimate aspects of students' lives to remember that rules of confidentiality are formulated *for the benefit of the student* and that they do harm if rigidly enforced when exceptionally critical situations arise. Appropriate modification is sometimes desirable.

A complex and as yet unsolved series of problems concerns the extent to which a college health service, and particularly its psychiatric division, should answer questions regarding the emotional status of students, even with their written permission. These questions are asked of the student by graduate schools to which they are applying for admission, and by committees considering applicants for Fulbright fellowships, Peace Corps jobs, and a variety of other governmental and private appointments. Some of the questions asked are reasonable, such as, "Do you have any health problem, physical, emotional, or mental which might interfere with your work if accepted?" If the answer is "yes," the applicant's physician may then be asked to submit information to the medical division of the agency involved. Other questions are totally unsatisfactory, such as, "Have you ever consulted a psychiatrist?" and should not be answered. Yet if no response to such an inappropriate and unfair question is made, the applicant will almost certainly be rejected.

One solution to the problem of confidentiality, even though a drastic one, is to stamp requests for information, as follows: "Blank College (or University) Health Service does not furnish health information about students for screening purposes. After acceptance, and with the student's permission, this form will be completed by this Department for your Medical Department." This would of course injure the interests of some students. This policy could hardly be adopted by one college or university alone, but would have to be something decided upon by the great majority of them, and new policies instituted in unison.

The purpose of such regulations, if they were installed, would be to call attention to the problem and to try to influence other institutions to follow suit. According to this theory, each institution should use its own methods of screening and not rely on information obtained from students in confidence.

The Harvard Law School has made it a policy not to ask for information which is derived from confidential sources. The idea behind this is that the Law School is perfectly capable of taking care of any persons who have hidden an illness manifestations of which appear after entrance. One point of view is that reducing the policy of the department to a set of rules or procedures would add to administrative problems and would harm more individuals than would leaving somewhat more latitude to each individual physician. Harvard College asks no questions regarding health of its applicants, although after they are admitted a communication is sent to the parents asking for whatever information they think may be helpful to the deans and to the medical department, and it is specified that this information will be kept confidential within those two departments.

Records should never be used for predicting performance in some unspecified area about which the physician or psychiatrist has no solid information. Even with extensive information, prediction of future performance is far from reliable. If students know that the records will be used for screening purposes, it is only reasonable that they should avoid seeking help when they need it. This aversion to seeking help is more noticeable in some institutions among premedical students than any other group. These people realize that the prejudice against anyone who has had psychiatric treatment or a psychiatric illness is very great in most medical school admissions committees.

Strict observance of all rules of confidence may not be helpful to all students. For example, a student who has fully recovered from an emotional disorder may ask a college physician to fill out a health form which constitutes a part of his application for a job or to a graduate school. The physician knows that giving all pertinent details will probably result in the student's failing to secure the desired appointment, there being strong prejudice against anyone who has had an emotional or mental illness. Withholding part of a medical record would not be ethical behavior. The college physician should make whatever dilemma that may exist clear to the student. The student might then go to a physician who had no access to his previous medical record and disclose only whatever information he chose to make known; he would do this on his own responsibility.

In the case of a student who had made a good recovery from an emotional illness, the examining physician could be expected to give a favorable statement regarding his health. A former patient who had not achieved reasonable stability might insist on a favorable recommendation regardless of his record, which a physician with access to his past history could not conscientiously give. In all such equivocal situations, a physician must try to be fair to the student (former patient) and yet remember that he has an obligation to the inquiring institution as well. He may fail to answer certain questions that he considers improper, but he cannot convey a false impression to aid a student. Since many of the issues which arise are not easily resolvable, the only recourse frequently available is the policy of being quite honest and frank in explaining the possible complications of any given course of action to all persons who may be affected by it.

It is obvious to anyone reading this chapter that the principles of confidentiality that apply to relations between students and faculty, administration and various types of counselors are far from complete. Definitive statements that will apply to any and all situations that may arise are probably impossible at present and perhaps always will be. In each new situation, the participants can only rely on their knowledge of how the clear-cut problems are usually handled (as outlined in this chapter); beyond that they must depend upon their innate sense of justice and fair play. As one of my colleagues said, in a moment of exasperation at overstrict attempts to maintain confidentiality, "Some one must strike a blow for common sense in this matter!" In general, the rights of the individual should be kept in the foreground. When decisions are made on the basis of what is best for the student in the long run, the institution can usually weather any criticism that may occur.

REFERENCES

1. CASS, L. J., AND CURRAN, W. T.: Rights of privacy in medical practice. *Lancet* (In press).
2. Griswold v. the State of Connecticut: *U. S. Law Week, 33*:4587, cited in Cass and Curran (*ibid*).

CHAPTER XII

RESEARCH

It is REGRETTABLE that a chapter on psychiatric research in colleges must consist largely of questions for which answers are needed rather than an account of confirmed results. The field is a relatively new one, and the more information the clinical workers compile the more numerous and complicated the questions become. My colleague, Mr. William G. Perry, Jr., Director of the Harvard Bureau of Study Counsel, was referring to this situation when he said that after many years of counseling students he was still ignorant but in a much more intelligent way than when he began his work.

Very few funds have been made available for psychiatric research on college students. Work in this area is accomplished mainly by clinicians who organize their experience and conclusions in their spare time. Most college psychiatrists are overwhelmed by clinical duties during their working hours, leaving little time for research. Since few psychiatrists are highly skilled in research methodology, the research projects they submit to government agencies and private foundations seldom win approval from the study groups who must examine them. Until one of the larger universities, utilizing the skills of clinicians cooperating with research workers in the behavioral sciences and in statistics, organizes a comprehensive research program, the gains in knowledge of the psychiatric aspects of college students' experience will continue to be haphazard and fortuitous.

Psychiatric research includes work done by psychiatrists on the clinical problems of students as well as on their normal development. Psychologists, sociologists, and other social scientists work more extensively in the latter area, but in any research undertaking collaborative efforts between psychiatrists and other social scientists are desirable when appropriate.

The many studies of campus cultures that have been carried out in recent years indicate a far greater activity (and support) for these projects than for strictly psychiatric research. The most comprehensive publication along these lines is Sanford's *The American College.*[1] Typical reports of the numerous conferences of workers in this field are *The Study of Campus Cultures*[2] and *Personality Factors on the College Campus.*[3] The bibliographies in these publications provide an approach to the vast literature of this field. The findings of research workers in this area are of immense significance to all college psychiatrists; in fact some of them are participating in these projects.

Research on college students, particularly if it involves parallel study of faculty members' influence on them, is beset with many difficulties. No faculty member wishes to be on record as being opposed to research. At the same time, it is understandable that he should be reticent about being a research subject himself, particularly when he has had no part in determining either the purpose or the methods to be employed. Objections commonly expressed include:

(1) The privacy of students and student-teacher relationships should not be invaded.

(2) A student may be made ill if he is asked about his adjustment problems.

(3) Forcing students to make choices in a multiple-choice type of test when no alternative is completely true is immoral or anti-intellectual.

(4) Information obtained concerning the college or any of its subdivisions may be harmful if published.

(5) If a break in secrecy occurs, data obtained in research projects may become general knowledge, subsequently harming individuals involved, particularly in later years when some of them have attained prominence.

(6) Students who are found to unusually vulnerable to emotional disorder may be forced into psychotherapy

against their wills or be discriminated against in some way.

(7) Research workers, particularly those with relatively little experience, often seem unaware of the scope and intensity of the issues they are studying, and when this is true, their results can be misleading.

Such objections must be taken seriously. Extreme care must be exercised to insure that all records containing intimate personal details be kept confidential. Published reports should be so organized as to avoid unnecessary harm to individuals whose roles in the research have not been praiseworthy. Research records should always be kept in secure places; only authorized persons should have access to them. When such precautions can no longer be carried out, the records should be destroyed. Premature publication of results (particularly of dramatic findings presented out of context) should be avoided. It is essential that, when projects or programs are being planned, the consent (when appropriate) or the assent of all persons who are to be involved is obtained.

The Committee on the College Student of the Group for the Advancement of Psychiatry has outlined the major areas in which research is currently being conducted. This report also contains a comprehensive bibliography.[4]

Clinical studies include work on improving the diagnosis and treatment of psychiatric disorders. Diagnosis of emotional disorders among college students is not yet satisfactory because their reaction to stress differs in various ways from that of other young people. Most students have not yet developed the characteristic features of the well-accepted psychiatric syndromes that are so often seen in patients much further along in their illnesses. It is not unusual for a psychiatrist new in college work to say that he sees patients whom he would not see in private practice or in a hospital clinic. They usually receive help at an earlier stage of their disabilities; many of them would never see a psychiatrist had they not come to college. The prognosis for students with psychoses is not so discouraging as many people think. Evidence gained from preliminary small studies suggests that the more sudden and outwardly disturbing the onset of the psychosis, the more favorable the outlook for recovery. If this can be confirmed on a large scale, with explicit descriptions of those with favorable and unfavorable prospects, new and better treatment can be developed for those patients requiring long-term care.*

A better system of diagnosis and classification of the emotional disorders of students is urgently needed, one less exclusively concerned with the classic psychiatric terminology, though consistent with it, and more revealing of the types of reaction to stress and the problems that engender them. Many students with severe problems can deal with them, with professional help, without developing frank neuroses or psychoses, and it is unfair to them to have such diagnoses made because of lack of flexibility of the official nomenclature.

Epidemiological studies done in various colleges have explored the factors common to certain illnesses or patterns of behavior, the causes of breakdown in the first year of college, the etiology and occurrence of suicide, the effect of separated parents on subsequent development of emotional disorder, and the special problems of medical students. College psychiatrists are often surprised and frustrated because, while their clinical impressions of the causes of emotional conflict in their student patients seem so clear, broad generalizations based on them often cannot be substantiated by existing statistical data. The factors which overwhelm one student may serve to goad another toward greater accomplishment. Extensive knowledge as to why the same stimuli may affect students in varying ways is urgently needed if students are to be taught how to deal with stress effectively. We greatly need a volume devoted to the research findings related to students that will help college personnel workers in the same way that Berelson and Steiner's *Human Behavior* serves all students of the behavioral sciences.[5] Much more research must be done before the material for such a volume is available for compilation, but a beginning could be made now.

Administrative studies involve those research projects de-

---

* See Carmen's study in Chapter IV and plan for comprehensive treatment of psychotic students in this Chapter.

signed to secure answers to specific problems about which
practical decisions must be made, with or without supporting
data. The need for extensive investigation is great, and the
questions that are being raised are numerous. Those of greatest
psychiatric interest include:

> What are the effects on the individual's emotional develop-
> ment of early admissions and advanced standing programs?
>
> Are present psychiatric services seeing the students who
> most need help or only those who might ultimately be able to
> solve their problems unaided?
>
> How can better case-finding methods be developed?
>
> How can applicants to college be screened to find those
> whose emotional status is such that failure is almost inevitable?
>
> What is the responsibility of a liberal arts college toward
> the development of emotional maturity in its students?

A *concept of personality* that will serve to organize and
assimilate the knowledge gained by observations of current student behavior is essential to all who are concerned with planning
college curricula and the development of new facilities. At present there is no such clear-cut concept that is accepted by all
educators. Most of them derive their ideas of the functioning of
the late adolescent and young adult from many sources, perhaps more from a retrospective analysis of their own experiences
at that period than any other. College psychiatrists tend to rely
on the basic tenets of psychoanalytical psychology, particularly
as elaborated by Erikson, more than on any other approach, but
they are constantly searching for new insights from any or all of
the behavorial sciences. As the GAP Committee states, "A
theoretical model of personality emerges which views behavior
as the ordered result of complex inter-relationships between
past experience, present situations, and future expectations. The
motivating forces involved are both conscious and unconscious,
and derive their power from instinctual drives as well as from
more rational ambitions and goals. This model does not supply
automatic explanations, but it does permit an approach to a
variety of difficult problems."[6] A college psychiatrists's reasonable hope is that this way of looking at behavior, which has been
so helpful to him in understanding students, may also be useful

to his colleagues in the academic departments of the college.

The *interaction between the student and the college* offers a potentially rewarding field for study. On arrival at college a student is a unique blend of all his past experiences, his biological characteristics, his particular style of adapting to new situations, and his expectations. In college, he meets countless other unique individuals, the traditions and expectations of the college, and the influences generated by parents, alumni, and the surrounding community. The student who finds the contrast between his past and his present too great may have his normal growth and development impeded by strong emotional conflicts. If the new conditions are so like the old as to make no new demands on him, he may become apathetic and complacent, overestimate his own capacity, and fail to develop as he should. A college environment that is characterized by insistence on high standards in every aspect of life, but with flexibility in how those standards are to be achieved, will produce quite a different reaction in most students from one which appears to them as rigid, dogmatic, inflexible, impersonal, and authoritarian.

The *educational process* itself is of intense concern to the college psychiatrist; he is especially interested in emotional responses to new audio-visual aids to learning, effects of various methods of increasing motivation (emphasis on grades, increased contact with teachers, freedom from set routines, honors courses, etc.), efforts to increase creativity, and ways of encouraging the student to assume early responsibility for his own intellectual development. Although the psychiatrist does not have exclusive knowledge of this field, he can aid his colleagues who do have the direct responsibility for introducing new educational methods by observing their effects on students.

Through the courtesy of my colleague, Dr. Stanley King, principal investigator of a study to determine methods by which Harvard students meet the obligations of a demanding course of study, a description of the research project follows.

The Harvard Student Study is a longitudinal research project dealing with changes in personality of random samples of Harvard College students as these students go through the four years of college. The goals of the project therefore are those of understanding personality change in late adolescence and early adulthood and of understanding the factors that are important in this change. In the latter case, the effects of the college and the background of the student are considered to be the important variables. The research project is divided into three subprojects, two of which deal with the study of individual students and the third of which deals with the characteristics of the environment in which they live, namely Harvard College.*

One subproject is known as the Panel Survey and uses as its source of subjects a 25 per cent random sample of the Classes of 1964 and 1965. Individuals in these samples were given an extensive battery of psychological tests and questionnaires, covering almost every facet of personality functioning and of behavior. The battery was given during the Freshman year, parts of it were repeated during the Sophomore and Junior, and the entire battery was readministered in the Senior year. The battery included standard psychological tests like the MMPI, the Strong Vocational Interest Blank, and the F Scale. It also included projective tests like the group Rorschach, the TAT, and some special fantasy measures devised for college populations.

A second subproject is known as the Case History Study. Subjects for this were selected from the random sample group in the Class of 1965. Thus, to a certain extent these subjects constitute a subsample. In addition to filling out all of the instruments in the Panel Survey, the subjects in the Case History study were interviewed periodically during each of their four years at Harvard and given a standard Rorschach during the Freshman, Sophomore, and Senior years and the standard TAT during the Freshman and Senior years. The interviews were tape-recorded and later converted to typescript. By balancing Survey methods with intensive studies, it is hoped that overall trends in personality change can be more fully understood or explained.

The third subproject is a study of Harvard College as a social system, with emphasis upon the residential living units,

---

* Supported by the National Institute of Mental Health with Additional support from the Hazen Foundation.

the Houses, and the academic departments. Essentially sociological in nature, this part of the research will describe the major goals of Harvard College and the ways in which these are implemented in the educational process. In addition, the differential aspects of subsystems within the College community can be assessed in relation to the kinds of personality change which are observed in students. Methods of data-gathering in this subproject have consisted of interviews with faculty members and administrative officials, observation of classes, and thematic content analysis of published materials about the College, including the College newspaper.

Data from the two classes have been processed and analyzed by computer techniques. Specific issues such as cognitive style, coping patterns, and ego interests are being investigated in the Case History data. The sociological analysis of Harvard College has reached the stage of theory development and forms the basis of two volumes now in preparation.

Few previous studies have elicited information about the individual and the social system in which he behaves. The Harvard Student Study provides an opportunity for investigating the close inter-relationship between these two phenomena. Educators will be interested in the extent to which various aspects of a college community can affect the lives of students and in the extent to which changes can be predicted from material about the student's background prior to his matriculation into college. College faculty and administrators have usually expected changes in students in attitudes and values and in cognitive style. The Harvard Student Study will be able to assess both of these areas of change and to indicate effectiveness of the college environment in producing such change. Of particular interest will be a determination of the adaptation process in late adolescence and early adulthood and of the extent to which various students undergo a period of crisis. Many theories are now predicated on the idea that the majority of students undergo crisis. Data affirming or disproving this theory would be of particular relevance to educators.

The reports on this study, both papers and books, will be published during the period from 1966 to 1970.

A procedure whereby the future academic performance of students can be predicted with reasonable accuracy is very much desired by all members of college admissions committees. In the writer's experience, the best guides presently available are: (1) the performance in secondary school as reflected in grades and standing with respect to classmates (weighted in accordance with previous experiences with students from the same school); (2) the expressed opinions of teachers and principals or headmasters, and (3) the college board scores. Occasionally, significant help in prediction of future performance is received from the report of an interviewer familiar with both the college and the home environment of an applicant.

Predictions concerning the ability of college applicants to maintain their emotional stability while in college are quite unreliable. Balser and his colleagues have for several years been perfecting an instrument for the prediction of mental disturbance in early adolescence. Using a chart to be filled out by teachers, they were able to predict the onset of serious emotional difficulties with an accuracy of 92 per cent in a group of 1712 students. Of this number, 236 were predicted to fail and 218 did so. They used the term "failure" to include any serious interference with the pupil's academic performance. Their chart included five different possible responses (by the teacher filling it out) on the following qualities or characteristics: motivation, industry, initiative, influence and leadership, concern for others, responsibility, emotional stability, significant school activities, truancy, academic average, adjustment, and age. There was no listing for sex, but boys were found to encounter sexual problems more often than did girls. Four teachers screened each child, preferably at the end of the first quarter of the ninth grade. The anonymity of each child predicted to fail was carefully guarded to avoid the self-fulfilling prophecy phenomenon.[7]

If relatively simple procedures could be devised to be given at college entrance to determine which students were most likely to develop emotional disturbances, preventive measures might be taken to aid such students. The use of such devices for screening purposes would raise ethical questions of considerable importance and probably should be avoided before admission. Research along these lines is urgently needed, though a variety of resistances would undoubtedly be encountered.

As I have indicated in Chapter V, the data regarding suicide among college students is scanty and generally unreliable. The estimate which seems as accurate as the sketchy facts permit is that there is a least one suicide for every 10,000 years of college attendance, which if extrapolated for the entire country means that we have about 500 suicides among college students each year. If the experience of the Los Angeles Suicide Prevention Center is accepted as valid for the colleges (i.e., that there are about six attempts for every successful suicide) this suggests that there are about 3,000 suicidal attempts by college students each year.

A national registry for data on suicidal attempts and successful suicides would be of great aid to those who plan preventive medical programs as well as to those who are concerned with the pressures experienced by college students. Obtaining reasonably accurate statistics regarding suicide would be relatively easy once a system of recording was devised. The statistics regarding unsuccessful attempts would be much more difficult. Why should this be so? Largely because it is often difficult to tell when a suicidal gesture is genuine or not. If a student takes one-half a lethal dose of a barbiturate, saying that he was restless and confused but unable to get to sleep and uncertain what the proper dose was, should this be considered a suicidal attempt? Or, if he jumps off a relatively low bridge in mid-winter, promptly swims to land, and says he had the impulse to jump but had no intention of committing suicide? These difficulties and uncertainties should not become a deterrent to establishing a central registry. The information requested from the colleges and universities should be relatively easy to report. For example, the reporting form might request:

> Number of suicides among students in the 1966-67 academic year. This would include all occurring during residence or among former students who had been registered during the year.

Number of attempted suicides while enrolled in college:
  a. Clear-cut suicidal attempts.
  b. Gestures that may not have represented genuine attempts.

A suitable location for the registry would be in the central headquarters of one of the national organizations most concerned with the problem, possibly the American College Health Association.

No reliable statistics are available to show how many college students become psychotic each year. Estimates by many college psychiatrists suggest that two to three students per 1000 enrolled have mental disturbances severe enough to require withdrawal from college. I have noted in Chapter IV that in a few relatively small samples more than half of these return to their original college and complete their studies. Occasionally, a student with a severe and prolonged illness, and whose parents can afford it, responds to skillful therapy over a long period; this suggests that more students with psychoses could be salvaged if appropriate treatment facilities were available.

A research program designed to test this hypothesis is urgently needed. Since the writer lives in New England and is most familiar with the colleges in that area, a program will be described which would be appropriate to conditions there.

A treatment center for psychotic students should be constructed in one of the large medical centers (Boston or New Haven) which would have many of the features of an educational institution as well as a mental hospital. It should be jointly sponsored by an already established teaching hospital and a university whose administration and faculty are sympathetic with the idea. It is especially desirable that many members of the faculty be interested because they will be called upon from time to time to aid in planning the educational program for the student patients.

The treatment staff would consist of college psychiatrists on the staff of nearby college health services as well as senior members of the staff of the sponsoring mental hospitals. Research projects designed to evaluate the effectiveness of treatment would be organized by teams of behavioral scientists.

The chief obstacle to the development of such a treatment and research unit is a financial one. Every possible source of funds should be explored—individual donors, foundations, the federal government, insurance plans of individual students, and payment of fees by parents of students when possible.

College women occasionally become pregnant when marriage is not possible or practicable. Their choices are relatively limited. A young woman may secure an abortion, she may bear the child and rear it in spite of the social handicaps involved, or she may bear the child and place it for adoption. What are the psychological results of each of these three measures? Legal, medical, religious, and social factors are complex in such situations, and there are not satisfactory solutions. But which are the least harmful to all persons concerned? Those who work out some course of action are faced with serious decisions, yet they have few solid facts on which to base them.

Those of us who work with college students soon come to believe that brief psychotherapy has its most promising application in connection with young persons whose symptoms are relatively new and whose intelligence is peculiarly helpful in developing insight into the nature and cause of their emotional conflicts. But is this really true or is it only wishful thinking? Could not research be devised that would give information as to the efficacy of brief psychotherapy? The obstacles would be numerous. Treating a portion of the students apparently needing help and ignoring the others would be disastrous for public relations. If the control group were informed of its role in such research, some members of it would be resentful, others might be stimulated to get help elsewhere, and some would probably investigate the nature of psychotherapy to see what they were missing and possibly achieve some benefit from their research. In any event, avoiding contamination of the central sample in the same institution would be difficult.

The psychiatrists who work in the relatively few psychiatric services with an adequate number of staff members have a responsibility to the smaller institutions to determine how their services can best help a college when the amount of time that can be given is small. Optimum division of work among social workers, clinical psychologists, and psychiatrists is one aspect of the problem; how a psychiatrist and his medical colleagues can best support faculty and upper classman counselors is another. Much research remains to be done on this problem if psychiatry is to aid college educators to the extent of which it is capable.

King has recently made a plea for the systematic acquisition of data about the emotional problems of students for the purpose of developing more effective programs of aid. Opinions differ as to whether or not emotional problems are increasing in numbers and in severity; no one can really speak authoritatively on this subject because of the lack of reliable data. All too many observers make broad generalizations based on their own restricted experience: "All Indians walk single file—at least the one I saw did." Systematic data gathering of the kind needed to plan productive research programs can be done with relatively limited funds if the facilities of an already existing organization can be utilized. King emphasizes that fact-finding studies should have highest priority. We need basic information on the nature and extent of the problem. The frequency of various symptoms and conflicts in different colleges is unknown. Information is needed about emotional problems as seen from both professionals' and students' points of view. The experiences of deans, tutors, advisors, and others who see students long before they reach the counselors' or psychiatrists' offices are also highly relevant.[8]

REFERENCES

1. SANFORD, N., Ed.: *The American College.* New York, Wiley, 1962.
2. LUNSFORD, T. F., Ed.: *The Study of Campus Cultures.* Boulder, Colorado, Western Interstate Commission for Higher Education, February 1963.
3. SUTHERLAND, R., *et al.,* Eds.: *Personality Factors on the College Campus.* Austin, Texas, Hogg Foundation for Mental Health, 1962.
4. Group for the Advancement of Psychiatry: *The College Experience: A Focus for Psychiatric Research.* New York, GAP Report No. 52, May 1962.

5. BERELSON, B., AND STEINER, G.: *Human Behavior: An Inventory of Scientific Findings.* New York, Harcourt, 1964.
6. Group for the Advancement of Psychiatry: *Op. cit.,* p. 734.
7. BALSER, B. H., WACKER, E., GRATWICK, M., MUMFORD, R. S., CLINTON, W., AND BALSER, P. B.: Predicting mental disturbance in early adolescence. *Amer. J. Psychiat., 121*: Supplement xi-xix, June 1965.
8. KING, S. H.: Emotional problems of college students: facts and priorities. *Amer. Ass. Univ. Professors Bull.,* Winter, 1964, pp. 327-332.

CHAPTER XIII

PREVENTIVE PSYCHIATRY

T HE APPLICATION OF concepts of preventive medicine exemplified by vast public health measures practiced throughout the world has been spectacularly successful, especially in the last half century. The reduction in the incidence of malaria and various parasitic infestations and improvement in sanitary habits are among the many reasons for the general increase in life expectancy. Improvement in maternal and child health practices have made possible the survival of millions of infants who would have died under earlier conditions. Much needless suffering has been avoided by these advances in health maintenance, but new problems have arisen as a result: the population crisis is the most serious of these. Improvements in health have not all resulted from the procedures of public health workers; many are the result of improved standards of living and more adequate education of the people involved.

In the meantime, mental and emotional disorders have been recognized as very serious issues. The American Medical Association has stated that mental illness is the major health problem now facing the nation and that "the medical profession has a clear responsibility to assume leadership in the mental health field and to work with professional and lay groups in a sustained, coordinated effort to effect sound, workable mental health programs."[1] Vast programs being undertaken in all the states and territories of the United States are designed to bring psychiatric treatment to all who need it, preferably as near their homes as possible to avoid the social dislocations so harmful to those who are admitted to isolated mental hospitals.

214

Those who have stimulated and developed these programs have been greatly impressed by the possibilities of applying preventive medicine and public health concepts to deal with mental illness and crippling emotional conflict. They realize that there are not, and never will be, enough psychiatrists, clinical psychologists, and social workers to give adequate treatment to all who need it. A combined approach, consisting of improvement of treatment of the mentally ill and coordination of the social and cultural conditions that contribute to the causes of mental illness and emotional distress, is being put into practice. Insofar as possible, efforts are being made to furnish whatever care is needed within the normal life context of the disturbed individuals. The term "community psychiatry" is frequently used to describe the whole movement, in spite of the fact that the term defies accurate definition.

Some readers may be confused as to the meaning of the term *mental illness,* as compared to *emotional illness* or emotional disorder. In this book, *mental illness* refers to those conditions in which the patient has become, as a result of long-continued stress, unable to judge reality accurately or to manage himself in such a way as to avoid disturbing others or harming himself. Such conditions as the psychoses (schizophrenia, manic-depressive psychosis, involutional melancholia, senile dementia, etc.) and the severe hysterias are mental illnesses. Some are caused by long-standing emotional conflict, some by biochemical and neurological abnormalities. *Emotional illness* refers to those conditions in which the individuals concerned are significantly handicapped by their conflicts but remain able to judge reality accurately and retain good contact with their environments. The term *neurosis* is applied to most of these disorders, especially when they have been present long enough to cause the patient to react in predictable ways. Not all emotional conflict or stress results in illness; everyone suffers from these, but most people are able to resolve conflicts constructively or learn to accept them when they are inevitable.

Many persons who have long been under emotional stress show its effects not by developing mental illness or neuroses but by acting impulsively against whatever restraint they may resent. They are said to "act out" their feelings, and are usually described as suffering from character disorders.

Most people, and parents of college students particularly, respond with more understanding and less anguish if their relatives are described as being "emotionally ill" or "emotionally disturbed" than "mentally ill." This is especially true before a definitive study has made an accurate diagnosis possible.

Since mental and emotional disorders are so common, the methods of treating them so expensive, and the people who are skilled in therapy so scarce, much consideration has been given to the idea of prevention on a massive scale. Many efforts have been made to show that prevention is possible; as yet there is no incontrovertible proof. Attempts to prove the efficacy of treatment have been no more satisfactory.

Primary prevention consists of efforts to reduce mental and emotional disorders by improving those conditions in a community which predispose its people to conflict and frustration. It also includes all those measures designed to enable people to cope more effectively with their problems (strengthen ego functioning). Theoretically, such measures should lower the incidence of new cases of mental disorder.

Secondary prevention refers to measures taken to insure early detection of emotional disturbance or mental illness, referral to appropriate sources of help, and treatment which diverts the individual from illness and impels him toward health.

Eisenberg has perceptively described some of the major difficulties faced by those who would promote preventive psychiatry.[2] The mental hygiene concept has not been proven effective. It is customary in many areas to deride the idea. Rules for healthy living seem not to be the answer. Some critics say, "Stick to individual treatment," but that is not adequate. Determinants of behavior include individual psychopathology as well as social and biological determinants. An important goal of the prevention-minded person is that of lowering the level of psychopathology in a community to permit a larger number (than otherwise) of people to handle the stresses to which they are exposed. All programs aimed at prevention may have unforeseen results in addition to those desired. For example, having more disturbed people in the community may increase the number of children with defective genes (if some kinds of mental illness are inherited) and their presence may cause psychological damage to children to whom they are intimately exposed.

Young people become predisposed to mental illness or retardation via intellectual understimulation, harmful interpersonal experiences, social psychopathology, and a lack of sense of continuity and tradition which renders them unable to rely on anything or anybody. Irreparable deficiencies may result from maldevelopment, malnutrition, injury, infection, and various complications that arise during pregnancy and childbirth, particularly prematurity. Thus, any program of primary prevention has wide ramifications. The present hope (according to Eisenberg) lies mainly in action to prevent socially-induced psychiatric illness through good housing, better health care, improved education, and a high level of employment—in short, programs based on concern for the welfare of everyone.

If the value of preventive psychiatry can ever be demonstrated, it should be possible to do so in the colleges. Young adults from seventeen to twenty-five, the ages of the majority of college and graduate students, are in that period in which the results of severe emotional stress have not yet become irreversible. Futhermore, their intellectual capacity and their openness to new ideas make them more than usually able to profit from brief psychotherapy. If they learn while in college which conditions make people more vulnerable to stress and which improve their ability to deal with stress successfully, they should (in theory) be more effective in their role as citizens in the communities in which they settle. Every progressive citizen should know which movements in his neighborhood deserve support, which should be opposed, and which should be altered to eliminate undesirable features. The process of finding out how people feel about the conditions under which they live consists largely of giving them an opportunity to be heard by community leaders who appreciate the role of emotions. If our college officials listen to the criticism of students, adapting their practices when constructive and practicable suggestions are received, they may teach students to act in similar ways when they in turn begin to assume positions of leadership. College mental health services can encourage such mutual exchange of opinions and, by so doing, aid students in increasing their self-knowledge, in becoming aware of how their actions affect others, and perhaps even in adding to their ability to bring up children with strength of character and personality.

The idea of preventive psychiatry is attractive to institutions of higher learning for a compelling reason: there is no possibility of obtaining enough professional help to meet the needs of students who have serious emotional conflicts. Methods of an educational nature must be found to deal with most of the quandaries in which students are involved. Whatever psychiatrists and their associates learn about the causes and results of the more serious emotional disturbances among students should be shared with counselors particularly and with all faculty members generally, so that their capabilities for dealing with many of the problems faced by normal students may be increased. The principles of confidentiality are never violated; individual privacy must always be respected. The facts learned from caring for those in conflict can be used in the correction of undesirable conditions and the improvement of extension of practices which have been shown, on a small scale, to have been advantageous in student maturation.

Some may decry the substitution of counselors, including many teachers with no special training in counseling, to do what psychiatrists and other highly trained professionals could presumably do better. It must be admitted that some teachers will be inept, some harmful, and some neutral, but many will develop skills and insight that will enable them to do almost as well as, or in some instances even better than, professionals. After all, the needs for psychiatrists in educational institutions arose because the harmful effects of previous disregard for the emotional aspects of learning and maturation became apparent. It is only logical that once psychiatrists, clinical psychologists, social workers, and other highly trained counselors demonstrate the need for teachers' involvement in all aspects of development, and show how this can be best achieved, they should focus their efforts on improving the educational process of the institution and its total impact on all its students, not just those who have serious disabilities. When this has been accomplished, there might be time to do a more adequate job with those students whose emotional crises are severe.

In the first international conference on the mental health of college students, held in 1956 with forty delegates from ten countries in attendence, much thought was given to possible methods of preventing mental illness and furthering mental health. The final recommendations could be repeated at a conference at present, ten years later, with equal relevance to current needs. Among these were:

1. Mental health programs should be the concern of everyone in the institution.

2. The programs should be geared to the normal educative processes of the institution.

3. Centers for training professional personnel should be set up in various countries in different parts of the world.

4. Special attention should be given to those who fail to complete their college educations.

5. Efforts should be made to help students get into colleges that are most suited to their needs and acceptable to them.

6. Instruction in marriage and family living should be freely available to students.

7. Research should be part of all mental health programs.

8. Administrators and teachers should be made familiar with the kinds of behavior that suggest mental or emotional disorder.

9. Students' views regarding university policy should be considered and, when practicable, students should be delegated considerable authority for their own self-regulation.

10. Loneliness should be combatted by helping students (particularly new ones) to develop attachments with others which give them a feeling of belonging.

11. Married students should have consideration of their special problems.

12. All students should be treated with equal dignity regardless of race, sex, color, or religion.[3]

An optimist can detect numerous indications that progress has been made in acting on these recommendations, but the progress has been uneven and quite inadequate when compared to the need.

The development of a program of prevention involves using procedures whose efficacy has not yet been proven beyond doubt. By its very nature, successful prevention destroys indications that anything has been prevented. Most psychiatrists agree that the evidence that mental illness can be prevented is far from conclusive. So far as I am aware, no college mental health program has ever been evaluated scientifically to determine its effects on the college. There is no clear consensus as to how this could be done. The traditional model of an experimental and a control group in such an evaluative attempt is unsuitable for several reasons: unfavorable public relations, spreading of influences from the experimental group to the control, and rapid changes in student body composition, among others. Like the problems of mental illness in the larger community, the need for some action concerning the mental health of students is so great that society cannot wait for exact and hence easy answers about etiology. The sad fact is that we are not using the knowledge we already possess about the care of the mentally ill to anything like the extent of which we are capable. Similarly, we are using mental health principles in colleges much less than I consider desirable. I will now try to suggest what colleges could do to improve the mental health of their students and at the same time improve the academic standards.

First, I will reflect on the clinical experiences I have had with students who have encountered distressing emotional conflicts and consider them in the light of tentative hypotheses derived from more general observations of behavior of college students. A few cardinal principles for reducing vulnerability to stress are significant for practical planning, even though adequate proof of their validity is not always present. We shall now examine some of these. These will be stated as desirable conditions to encourage in any college which wishes its students to become adept in handling emotional conflicts while they are at the same time acquiring intellectual power.

Repeated challenges to the student's ability, each of which can be mastered after sustained effort. Without stress and stimulation, little is learned. Ideally, as Ralph Barton Perry stated, "The more one learns the more one has to learn with." The student who acquires a particular point of view which he thereafter defends with great intellectual skill against any and all challenges from others has failed to acquire a liberal education. He has merely become a technologist with words and ideas and can respond only with difficulty to new and varied circumstances.

Maintenance of high standards of academic performance and personal behavior but with flexibility as to how these standards may be attained. Principles rather than rules are emphasized. Thoughtfulness concerning behavior rather than preoccupation with legalisms is encouraged. What students may become is considered on an equal basis with their behavior at any given time.

Assurance that when significant changes in thinking and behavior are required of students sufficient time is allowed for suitable adaptation, if possible under conditions which add to, not decrease, their self-confidence. Abrupt policy changes, made unilaterally by the administration or any other group, tend to increase and harden hostile and rebellious tendencies that may heretofore have been motivated by other factors, permitting them to be concentrated against the college. This may seriously impair learning: under these circumstances, making a poor record becomes a weapon in the struggle against authority.

Avoidance of breaks in continuity of behavior that are too abrupt for the student to master unaided, or provision for protracted help in making such an adaptation once the over-great contrast is recognized. Among the examples that come readily to mind are: the student with language deficiencies, the person who comes from a relatively simple society with rigidly held values to a college where pronounced liberal views are predominant, the student for whom variations in cultural patterns between the home and college communities are quite marked, and the brilliant student who has never been challenged and as a result has never acquired the capacity for sustained intellectual effort.

Developing among faculty members understanding attitudes toward and reliable information about their students together with the opportunity for frequent constructive dialogues between students and faculty members on subjects of mutual interest. The growing trends toward impersonality and mechanization in education, and lack of time of both faculty and students, is weakening some of the motivational influences that most strongly encourage a high order of intellectual effort. If every teacher could in some way contrive to spend two hours weekly in informal but constructive contacts with individual or small groups of students, the educational process would be immeasurably enriched. An excessive amount of the faculty member's time is not needed, the encounters that do occur should be conducive to learning.

Efforts by college psychiatrists, psychologists, social workers, and all other counselors to encourage more of the problem-solving or emotional maturation experiences of students to take place within the educational rather than the therapeutic setting. In psychiatry, we are becoming accustomed to the concept of the community's influences having a therapeutic effect. Likewise, we must look upon the college as an agency which teaches and encourages emotional maturation simply by the exhibition of emotional stability by its representatives. This ideal can be furthered by the use of whatever psychiatric talent may be available in working with college officials and teachers on matters of emotional import, rather than confining its use to the treatment of those students who have become ill. Psychiatric skills for such activity are not the same as those most effective in therapy, but skill in individual psychotherapy is an essential prerequisite for working appropriately with administrators and teachers.

The following case history (and partial analysis) will serve to show how a few visits with a psychiatrist (or other competent counselor) may prevent the development of still more serious difficulty in a student who is very concerned about herself.

An eighteen-year-old freshman in a coeducational college with high academic standards came to the college psychiatrist at the suggestion of her parents, whom she had called one night when she was feeling lonely, homesick, and plagued with troublesome thoughts and feelings. Her intent had been to call home and tell her parents not to expect to hear from her for a while as she had some things to work out in her own mind. But in the middle of the conversation, she suddenly began crying. Her parents were very sympathetic and understanding, offered to come to see her if she felt the need (which she didn't), and as an alternative suggested that she consult the college psychiatrist.

At the first interview it was noticed that she was quite attractive, very feminine, and slightly shy. She said that now that she was in the psychiatrist's office she hardly knew why she had come to see him. She appeared somewhat anxious and frightened but otherwise, in manner and character, she was the very prototype of a wholesome, all-American girl next door. It was obvious that she was quite bright and very articulate as she discussed her problem.

She complained of mental discomfort and uneasiness characterized by feeling tense and jittery at times, especially when she had papers to write and when tests were approaching. These symptoms, and cessation of menstruation, began early in the school year and had continued for several months until her visit to the psychiatrist.

These episodes of anxiety and tension were usually accompanied by introspective preoccupations, with certain thoughts and feelings of which she had previously not been aware. For the first time in her life, she became aware of aspects of her personality that she found objectionable; she did not want to admit their presence but thought that she should. For example, she felt guilty about what she regarded as the distorted picture other people had of her and which she had of herself, particularly in terms of not being as good as she imagined and would have liked herself to be.

At times, she indulged in much self-questioning: "Who am I? What am I? Where am I going in life?" She was aware of the ubiquitous character of these very common "identity" questions, which nearly every college student asks himself at some time or other. But she was rather intolerant that she was subject to the same self-inquiry. Her past values were coming into question and she was plagued by doubts about religion, the existence of God, and certain moral questions. She wondered if religious worship might help with some of the problems and questions growing in her mind, but she refused to pray as she had done in the past for fear that it would not work and thus might confirm her doubts.

The main problem associated with these complaints was that the local college scene and atmosphere were completely unlike anything she had ever known before. As a result she had become mildly anxious and depressed because of this new and unpleasant situation, which required new adjustments and shifting some previously held ideas and values to make room for different ones.

She was born and raised in a community in a totally different region and climate from that of the college. Her family was very close-knit, warm, devoutly Protestant, and strictly adherent to traditional moral values and ethics.

Before college she had been regarded by family, friends, neighbors, and teachers as the ideal type of girl, and she had so regarded herself. Her behavior had always been exemplary, and she had never questioned her values and standards. She had dated one boy fairly regularly in high school, and the relationship was more brother-and-sister than boy friend and girl friend.

At college she had dated a number of boys, but no one had ever really made a pass at her because, as she said of herself, "I am not the sort of a girl boys have ever made passes at." She virtually had been a girl on a pedestal, to look at and admire, but untouchable. At college, she felt conflicts about her dating habits and vowed to become even more selective and not to date just anyone in order to get out on Saturday night, as many of her girl friends did.

However, surrounding her were girls with less conservative attitudes and thoughts about religion, sex, etc., and many of these ideas were direct opposites of her own code of morality. Her roomate was a wealthy, sophisticated, smart, and "modern thinking" girl from a big city who was having an affair under unusual circumstances with a boy from a nearby college, the details of which she discussed freely with the patient. She was supporting her boy friend in high style in order to maintain his affection. The patient openly disapproved of her roomate's behavior, and both of them agreed that the roommate might need help. In spite of the fact that the patient was quite alarmed and disquieted by her roomate's revelations about her problem, behavior, and values, which were quite at variance with her own, they continued to be good friends.

The patient was seen in short-term psychotherapy at weekly intervals for several visits. At the end of the first interview, she expressed considerable relief at having been able to talk about the disturbing questions with someone she could trust. In the subsequent visits, she appeared calm and relaxed as she continued to discuss various feelings and conflicts which revealed an extremely strict conscience and guilt about her feeling that she had been favored over her younger brother by her father and had been more popular and successful in school than he. Also, she had been scrupulously honest as a child and now she felt quite guilty about occasionally picking up an unclaimed pencil or raiding the dormitory refrigerator. At her final visit, she appeared bright and cheerful and said that she again felt like her old self. She was able to study more effectively, her menstrual periods began for the first time in four months, and she had become active in certain school extracurricular activities. She was relieved that her roomate had also followed her suggestion of seeking professional help.

This case brings up many interesting points —
    (1) Her values were questioned.
    (2) Her parents stood behind her.
    (3) She kept open the lines of communication with her roommate.
    (4) She looked at herself rather than running with the crowd.
    (5) She was unashamed to seek help.
She might have —
    (1) "Experimented" against her better judgment.
    (2) Made a suicidal gesture.
    (3) Turned against her parents.
    (4) Resorted to inappropriate religious habits.

(5) Withdrawn from ordinary activity.
(6) Tried escape into overwork.
(7) Developed a neurosis.

One could wish that methods of handling such situations as the one illustrated here were more prevalent, but it is encouraging that they are becoming more widespread. The psychiatrist served as a tutor in an area of personal development not always considered a concern of higher education.

Any college psychiatrist who observes his institution closely soon becomes aware that basic sentiments among students, usually summarized by the term *peer-group pressures*, have a strong influence in determining their motivation. Whereas there are strong influences stemming from a variety of sources that attract students to a life of the intellect, these pressures are all too often in conflict with even stronger attractions that are basically anti-intellectual. Approval of "getting by" on a gentleman's C (not as strong as it once was), emphasis on social activities, many of the attitudes encountered in fraternities and sororities (where there may be more emphasis on grades than on the learning they should represent), commercialization of athletics, undergraduate fads of various kinds— these and many others are antithetical to the development of intellectual habits.

Many students enter college highly motivated toward the pursuit of learning for its own sake only to fall victim to that pseudosophistication, so prevailing in undergraduate atmospheres and characterized by a considerable superciliousness, which is at once extremely attractive and actively inhibiting to a life of the mind. Those who exhibit this quality are often smooth and convincing, and may be quite unaware that they possess it. They may say, "You don't have to crack a book around here." although they may study quite hard when not being observed. They talk endlessly of their exploits, emphasizing their familiarity with all kinds of esoteric experience. They ridicule simple and direct attitudes, frequently making fun of the most respected values held by the new student. In all areas of complex human behavior, they act as if they already knew the answers, effectively preventing their own further learning about them. Gamesmanship, rather than sincerity, is their ideal. Most students recover from this disorder, although a few do not. Obviously, no person exhibits all these undesirable traits, but the collective effect of many who exhibit some of them can be both anti-intellectual and antisocial. The wise student will make his own decisions in terms of his own goals and ideals, rather than be pushed around by the pseudosophisticated. But it takes courage to do this.[4]

To add to these negative pressures, the preponderance of attitudes displayed by the mass media of communication (with a few notable and refreshing exceptions) is one of derogation of intellectual life; style, appearances, and one-upmanship are valued more than sincerity, commitment, or genuine effort. The nature and extent of these pressures, which determine the extent of the success of their best efforts, should be constantly studied by faculty members.

REFERENCES

1. A.M.A.: *Program of the Council on Mental Health.* 535 Dearborn St., Chicago, p. 1.
2. EISENBERG, L.: Preventive psychiatry—if not now, when? *Amer. J. Orthop., 32*:781-793, 1962.
3. FUNKENSTEIN, D. H., Ed.: *The Student and Mental Health—An International View.* New York, World Federation for Mental Health, 1959, pp. 419-426. (This volume is obtainable only from the World Federation for Mental Health, 124 E. 28th St., New York.)
4. FARNSWORTH, D. L.: Commencement address, *Horace Mann Alumni Bull.,* Summer, 1965.

CHAPTER XIV

PSYCHIATRY AND VALUES

T HROUGHOUT THIS BOOK, I have attempted to show why the emphasis in higher education should be changed from exclusive preoccupation with the accumulation, transmission, and storage of information to a greater consideration of the factors which enable the individual to be free to use his mind as he wishes and to motivate him to use it constructively. It is in the attainment of this latter desideratum that the question of which values should be most strongly upheld becomes crucial.

Among educators, there is growing acceptance of the idea that increasing the intellectual power of an individual without developing a corresponding degree of self-control and responsibility may be disastrous. We have for too long held the fond hope that more education, in terms of increasing our citizens' general store of knowledge, would lead to a solution of all our problems. Reflection on events of the last few decades, with their two world wars initiated by a country with one of the highest levels of education in the world, gives little support to this idea. The development of character and integrity of the highest quality should be prime goals of education.

Values which responsible men and women in our society assume to be practically universal are frequently unclear to many of our young people. We have too many high school and college students who are "moral illiterates." Indeed, a sense of meaning and purpose is missing even in the lives of many of our older people. Schools and colleges cannot afford to overlook opportunities for developing constructive and satisfying values in students.

So far as the colleges are concerned, their major task is to transmit values from the older generation (the faculty) to the younger (the students). The chief emphasis in the past has been on intellectual values. A college that appears to have a narrow and rigid concept of values probably stultifies the intellectual and emotional growth of many of its students. A college that seems to have no commonly accepted values can do little more for its students than a set of encyclopedias could do, but it could be harmful to their development.

The definition of *moral* on which I will base this discussion is: "characterized by excellence in what pertains to practice or conduct: springing from, or pertaining to, man's natural sense or reasoned judgment of what is right and proper."[1] From another source, *value* (a term almost always associated with moral) is defined as: "that which is worthy of esteem for its own sake; that which has intrinsic worth."[2]

Some of the values about which psychiatrists, as well as all mental health proponents, are particularly concerned are knowledge, tolerance, sympathy for the unfortunate, flexibility, capacity to love and be loved, thoughtfulness for others, respect for the dignity of every human being, concern for the young, esteem for the scientific method, preference of morality to immorality, and many others of similar nature.

It is not unusual (in fact, it is almost routine) for any group of persons with diverse backgrounds in psychiatry, psychology, philosophy, or theology (to mention only a few possibilities) who attempt to discuss values and morals (or character and personality) to end with no agreement on anything—definitions, methods of teaching desirable qualities, what the desirable qualities are, or anything else. Yet each discussion seriously pursued clarifies certain concepts for most of the participants.

For many reasons psychiatrists, as well as most other behavioral scientists, have been very cautious about becoming involved in issues that suggest that they hold definite ideas about morality, yet so far as I have been able to observe psychiatrists are very much concerned with morals. To be accused of being a "moralist" is to be charged with intolerance or a narrow view of life. Yet, psychiatrists are concerned with morals, morality, and values with every patient they treat. Even though they are as concerned with morals and values as any professional group, their general attitudes are frequently misunderstood. This may in part be due to the impression of many people that psychiatrists are opposed to religion. Some of them undoubtedly are, and in ways more offensive than are necessary. Many others, however, are not only religious in their personal lives but are working closely with members of the clergy in developing and improving methods of collaboration between their two disciplines for the benefit of the people they serve. A good psychiatrist does not permit his lack of religious belief to intrude into treatment nor prevent him from encouraging it, if appropriate, in his patients. A psychiatrist who opposes or derides religion does so on his own responsibility, and not with the backing of the profession to which he belongs.

Freud's opposition to religion had much to do with causing strong hostility to psychoanalysis in its early phases, as well as at the present time when the nature of psychoanalysis, psychodynamics, and psychiatry are still confused in the minds of many people. Zilboorg has brilliantly analyzed Freud's hostility to religion, pointing out that his attitudes were at times ambiguous on the subject. For example, in *Civilization and Its Discontents*, he said, "Nor may we allow ourselves to be misled by our own judgments concerning the value of any of these religions or philosophic systems or of these ideals; whether we look upon them as the highest achievement of the human mind, or whether we deplore them as fallacies, one must acknowledge that where they exist, and especially where they are in the ascendant, they testify to a high level of civilization."[3] It should also be noted that whereas Freud thought of religion as an illusion, he personally adhered to very high moral standards. In a letter to Freud, Oskar Pfister (a Zurich pastor and psychoanalyst) said, "If you would fuse your own contribution with the great world harmony, like the synthesis of notes in a Beethoven symphony into a musical whole, I could say of you 'There never was a better Christian.'"[4] To Pfister he said, " In itself, psychoanalysis is neither religious nor the opposite, but an impartial instrument which can serve the clergy as well as the laity when it is used only to free suffering people."[5]

Collaborative efforts between psychiatrists and members of the clergy of all faiths have now become common; members of each discipline are learning from the other without impairing their own professional identities, but there are some risks involved.[6]

Some critics of psychiatry base their opposition on the behavior of certain psychiatrists whose actions they do not approve. It is true that so much is now expected of psychiatrists that any deviation from the expected, whether in the form of emotional disorder or behavior evoking criticism from the community, is interpreted in a way derogatory to the whole profession. Regrettable as such lapses may be, it must be remembered that members of other professions also do not always succeed in living up to the standards of their profession. Yet, the effort must always be made. One of our most revered elder statesmen in psychiatry, Dr. Stanley Cobb, has said:

"If we psychiatrists are to help our patients to achieve more mature and altruistic ways, it is obvious that we must have solved, as far as possible, our own personal problems, for psychotherapy is a two-way street. When we became physicians, we undertook an obligation to place service to our patients, to other physicians, and to society above our personal desires. Particularly, the psychiatrist who deals with problems of human behavior is obligated to support moral standards."[7]

In Jacob's study on values of college students, he stated that American college students tend to think alike, feel alike, and believe alike.[8] He concluded that the influences of colleges on the values upheld by their students was much weaker than most of their administrators appeared to believe. A few colleges were noted to have "a peculiar potency," and most of these had a distinctive educational mission, something subtle and rather unpredictable but certainly not resulting from chance. There were few of them. Thus, Jacob concluded that the values of the mass of students would be determined largely by the public institutions.

The student attitudes that have received the most public notice in the last decade have indeed been those characteristic of the large state universities. Impersonality, decreased emphasis on counseling, fewer opportunities for close faculty-student relations, less emphasis on teaching and more on research, are all allegations heard with greatest frequency on the most crowded campuses. The application of ideas of mass production derived from industrial experience does not appear to be working as well in education as it did in business and industry. There may well be no substitute for meaningful personal relationships between older and younger colleagues in a college if values are to be changed in a desired direction.

A study by Vreeland and Bidwell[9] of the organizational effects of student attitudes exerted by the Harvard Houses showed that the Houses do indeed affect student values and attitudes. Although they caution against overinterpretation of their results until their studies are replicated, they suggest that the affective climate of a House is the central mechanism of value and attitude change. The amount (extensity) of student change is highest in those Houses which have an integrated peer social structure and is lessened by any inconsistency in the value environment, whether through disagreement of Master and Staff or either group with student leaders. Thus, when the attitudes of the Master and the House staff are divergent, the effect on student attitude changes is not as extensive as when they are congruent. The tutors as a source of cross-pressure are less powerful than the House Master. When the students form a contra-culture, but lack an integrated social structure, value and attitude change is toward staff goals. "Thus the question of college potency involves not only the strength of the affective bond between student and college, but also the consistency of the college environment. Environmental consistency, however, is not an outcome simply of a homogeneous membership. The beliefs of faculty, student influentials, and student sub-groups, as well as the manner and force by which these beliefs are transmitted through the social structure, presumably bear unequally and interactively upon environmental consistency."

The formation and perpetuation of consistent college environments depend upon the selection of students and the impact of student "influentials" upon their fellows, notably across student generations. If these are similar from year to year and "conforming sub-cultures" are formed, staff and student influence become consistent and reinforcing, rather than conflicting and mutually weakening.

One might postulate from these findings that if a college is to have an effect upon its students in promoting any particular values or attitudes that are considered desirable, much attention should be paid to gaining a reasonable and flexible concensus of their desirability among administration, faculty, and students. Propagandists for vicious causes have learned how to promote a concensus in a given population, even for causes which relatively few individuals initially thought desirable. It remains to be seen whether institutions of higher learning can effectively inculcate values and attitudes that promote dignity and respect for all persons and at the same time enhance the intellectual development of all their students.

I have long been baffled by the complexity of the task of determining how to set about facilitating emotional maturity in the majority of our students, supplementing that small minority that seems to attain this quality without conscious effort. Exhortation is of little value. Developing a sufficiently high percentage of persons of high integrity and understanding would furnish an environment in which young people might acquire those same qualities almost automatically. Unfortunately, the balance of forces in most communities is more strongly supportive of self-centeredness and prompt impulse expression than of appropriate concern for others and the delay of instinctive desires until their satisfaction is not harmful to others. Ideally, the methods for developing emotional maturity should be supported by the family, churches, schools and colleges, the mass media of communication, and peer group pressures. Instead, these sources of authority and influence are tragically divided, with some of them being conducive to emotional immaturity even as they are anti-intellectual.

Since more than a quarter of all our people are enrolled in educational institutions, a program suitable for application in them should theoretically have a perceptible effect. Elsewhere, I have outlined a series of goals of education which might appropriately supplement those traditionally in vogue for the attainment of intellectual proficiency. These may be considered as values as well as goals. They are as follows:[10]

1. Respect for all persons, regardless of their race, color, ethnic background, religion, or behavior at the moment.

2. Sufficient knowledge of other people to be able to judge in a general way what their needs are, the ideals they honor, the customs they practice, and the frustrations they endure.

3. Knowledge of the qualities required in a person who can be at home with diverse groups of people and yet be able to enjoy being alone.

4. A sensitive and perceptive awareness of one's own nature, both those qualities under the control of the will and those which are not.

5. Sufficient modesty and humility not to feel impelled to impose one's own ideas on others.

6. The achievement of a proper balance between self-regard and a concern for the welfare of others.

7. The ability to appreciate how one's own self is perceived by others, thereby enabling the individual to modify his own actions continually in order to increase his competence and capacity to relate to others.

8. The quality of being able to disagree with others without becoming angry; a conviction that differences of opinion should be settled by the power of rational authority rather than by force, whether verbal or physical. At the same time the value, even the necessity, of righteous (or judicious) indignation should be realized.

9. The habit of inquiry and doubt, practiced in such a way as not to become either a fanatic who sees simple solutions to complex issues or a cynic who sees no merit in any constructive activity.

10. Capacity to formulate the nature of problems not yet apparent and ability to plan the development of appropriate solutions.

Obviously, these could not be taught directly, but they should serve as starting points for discussion of the intricate processes by which young people acquire values from others. Even when they evoked opposition, as they inevitably would in many situations, the attempt to define better goals would be constructive.

In the following chapter other aspects of the problem of psychiatry and values are discussed.

REFERENCES

1. *Webster's New International Dictionary,* 2nd Ed., 1934.
2. *Shorter Oxford English Dictionary.*
3. ZILBOORG, G.: *Psychoanalysis and Religion.* New York, Farrar, Straus and Cudahy, 1962, pp. 25-26.
4. JONES, E.: *The Life and Work of Sigmund Freud,* Vol. II. New York, Basic Books, 1957, p. 199.
5. —————: *The Life and Work of Sigmund Freud,* Vol. III. New York, Basic Books, 1957, p. 352.
6. EWALT, J. R., AND FARNSWORTH, D. L.: *Textbook of Psychiatry.* New York, McGraw-Hill, 1963, pp. 299-311.
7. COBB, S.: Machines, medicine, and morals. *Amer. J. Psychiat., 121*:1212-1213, 1965.
8. JACOB, P.: *Changing Values in College.* New York, Harper, 1957, pp. 1-11.
9. VREELAND, R., AND BIDWELL, C.: Organizational effects on student attitudes: a study of Harvard Houses. *Sociology of Education, 38*:233-250, 1965.
10. FARNSWORTH, D. L.: *The Search for Identity.* A lecture in press. Forest Hospital, Des Plaines, Illinois.

CHAPTER XV

THE ROLE OF PSYCHIATRY IN THE CONTEMPORARY WORLD*

Psychiatry is presently undergoing a significant change in concepts and methods. Until the last few decades, it concerned itself almost exclusively with the study and treatment of abnormal behavior. Gradually, however, it has become apparent to psychiatrists that abnormal behavior could be understood only when the conditions which govern those who remain well are also known. Of necessity, therefore, the boundaries of psychiatry's interests have expanded to include everything human; yet the essential task of psychiatry remains that of understanding and modifying those actions, thoughts, and feelings that interfere with optimum functioning. In other words, its interest lies primarily in how and why man fails to achieve what he is capable of achieving.

Psychiatry is not a systematic philosophy. All psychiatrists make certain assumptions about man: that he is neither inherently good nor bad at birth but has enormous potentialities for being both, that his behavior can on the whole be understood, and that he can in large measure determine whether he is to be basically good or evil, effective or ineffective, constructive or destructive. These assumptions permit many philosophic positions, and individual psychiatrists and patients maintain a wide variety of attitudes toward politics, religion, the arts, and other vital questions.

------

* Reproduced with minor changes by permission from *The Person in Contemporary Society*, a symposium on the occasion of the dedication of the Memorial Library, University of Notre Dame, May 7, 1964. Privately printed.

A child at birth is a creature with many possibilities. The things he may do in his lifetime are almost infinite in their scope and variety, yet he cannot go beyond the limitations set for him by his sex, his physical constitution, his intellectual capacity, and the particular genetic characteristics with which he is endowed. Ordinarily, he cannot even approach these limits because of still other restrictions inadvertently imposed on him by himself and by the society or culture in which he lives.

These limitations usually seem clear to professional workers who spend their lives dealing with their effects. Yet, for reasons which are obscure but powerful, there is a pervasive unwillingness on the part of those in charge of community improvement projects to recognize these handicaps although they are the very ones whose decisions might lessen their harmful results.

A person is, to a great extent, the sum of his inheritance, his constitution, and his experiences. Yet, this does not mean that he must be what he is; he has the power of choice or free will. The range of choice for an individual may be a narrow one, but the fact that it exists is of the highest significance.

Psychiatrists do not necessarily look upon perfect adaptation to one's environment as evidence of good emotional health. Certainly, adaptation to humiliating conditions in a passive, dependent way is not desirable, especially when this course renders the individual ineffective and deprives him of satisfaction from his life and work. Constructive rebellion or refusal to adapt to unacceptable situations may be the essence of good emotional health.

One of the most intense or potent inhibiting influences against the full use of one's capacities is a feeling of rejection. An unwanted child whose parents fail to communicate love and affection to him can only project his unhappiness about this rejection onto others who seem to him indifferent to his needs. If a child has no parents to care for him and the parental substitutes are unable to convey a feeling of warmth, he tends to become suspicious and constricted in his capacity to relate to others in a satisfying way.

When a child who has already experienced varying degrees of rejection encounters exclusion or disapproval because of personal characteristics over which he has no control—a physical disability, for example, or membership in an unpopular minority group, or the color of his skin—his lack of confidence in himself becomes greater. Prejudice expressed as unfair discrimination is regrettable, not only because of its effects on the victims but also because of its disintegrative influence on the characters of those who practice it.

Intimately related to the attitudes of rejection shown by persons toward one another are the feelings of hostility that result. Human beings are constituted in such a way that they tend to respond in kind to whatever attitudes are shown toward them, especially in their formative years. Friendliness begets friendliness, suspicion fosters more suspicion, and hostility provokes reciprocal hostility.

People who feel rejected and are the objects of hostility from their fellows may react in various ways, but they all become more isolated and withdrawn. Those who want isolation for personal reasons may get comfort and satisfaction from it, but those on whom isolation is forced suffer its harmful effects.

Clinical evidence from the case histories of emotionally troubled children and adults as well as the studies of historians, social scientists, and students of government indicate that rejection, hostility, unfair discrimination, and unwanted isolation are extremely damaging to both individuals and society at large. Although their origins can often be plainly seen, their mitigation or elimination have thus far defied all efforts of men of good will. Wherever massive efforts have been made to alter their effects, powerful vested interests appear to thwart these attempts. It is a truism—but still valid—that man is his own worst enemy. He has failed to apply the knowledge he possesses about character development of the individual.

Young people do not formulate ethical principles and then act in accordance with them; they emulate their elders and gradually learn what kind of behavior brings them approval. Young people who do not get approval from their elders will seek it from their peers; if their healthy and socially constructive undertakings are not rewarded, they will engage in destructive activities to attract attention. The importance of good role

models is crucial. Children whose parents are worthy of emulation, and who love and cherish them, and apply firm and appropriate discipline consistently, are fortunate indeed. As yet, no
institutional environment exists that seriously challenges the
family's effectiveness in guiding children through the tumultuous
years of infancy, childhood, and adolescence and introducing
them to the responsibilities of adulthood. Yet, many parents who
have provided a strong and well integrated family life find that
many of their best efforts are nullified when their children enter
into undesirable associations with others of their own age groups.
Children develop best if the ideals of their own and neighboring
families and those of the schools and churches are in reasonable
harmony.

The public or institutionalized results of the undesirable
attitudes we have been discussing appear most often in neighborhoods of inferior quality. In them the schools are poor, housing
is inferior, recreational facilities are inadequate or inappropriate,
and religious sentiment is weak. The secularization of a community may well signal the beginning of deterioration in the
quality of living in a community. In the classical studies by
Leighton and his colleagues of Stirling County, Nova Scotia,
pronounced secularization was found to be associated, either as
a cause or an effect, with hostility, malignant gossip, bootlegging,
stealing, sexual promiscuity, and other evidences of social
disintegration.[1]

Psychiatry has traditionally concentrated on a somewhat
restricted view of the problem—the late effects of any combination of these harmful influences on individuals have been its
major preoccupation.

People become ill when they have exhausted their personal
resources for dealing with the stresses which they have encountered. Since so many of these stresses are invisible (are
emotional conflicts within the individual), they often are not
intelligible to the untrained observer. The behavior of the
distressed person frequently excites revulsion, hostility, embarrassment, or rejection rather than sympathy, compassion, and a
desire to help, as does physical illness or injury. Furthermore,
since all persons have varying degrees of conflict, frustration,

and repressed desires, exposure to an obviously troubled person often arouses distressing anxiety, especially in the individual who sees in the troubled person a reflection of some of his own problems.

Although each person responds in a unique manner to the particular constellation of troubles which have beset him, there are a few general patterns of reaction which occur with great frequency and are referred to by psychiatrists and their colleagues as neuroses, psychoses, character disorders, or psychosomatic symptoms (with a variety of subdivisions in each category). Overdependence upon these diagnostic labels can create obstacles to clear thinking. The current trend in psychiatry is to place primary emphasis on the attempt to understand every factor that has been influential in interfering with the patient's effectiveness, rather than on giving a name to the disorder. This does not mean that making a diagnosis is less important than it has ever been, but rather that the concept of what constitutes a diagnosis has been broadened.

Every human being is caught in a complex web of events, one or more of which may be his undoing at any moment. In earlier times, our planet was much less crowded than now, but the dangers presented by external events were much more obvious. The principles of medicine and public health were largely unknown and man was threatened at every turn by disease, injury, and early death. Plagues, destroying vast numbers of people, were common. Without modern advances in agriculture and skill in the preservation of foods, hunger and malnutrition were rampant, not only during droughts or floods but also in the late winter and spring months for those who lived outside the torrid zones. Since education, knowledge of scientific methods, and effective communication were lacking, superstition gave rise to, and in turn was used to deal with, many irrational fears. Economic depression and exploitation of the weak by the strong were accepted as unavoidable. Though suffering was intense and frequent, there was usually an ascribed cause, an external reason (though it might be a false one), and man was reconciled to this cause through his assumption that there was nothing he could do about it.

Now man has an entirely different attitude toward the cause of his woes. He is still caught in the tangle of events, but he considers that for every baleful development which threatens or harms him there is a cause which can be delineated and some-one who is responsible for it. If the physician had only used a different drug or another procedure, the patient would not then have died. The public health authorities could have prevented the epidemic had they been more alert. The government officials should have foreseen a crop failure and have stockpiled substitutes for scarce items. Acceptance of the scientific method has led to the expectation that everything is possible. Superstition due to lack of education and poor communication has been replaced by surfeit and boredom from massive dissemination of ideas, many of them not worth transmitting. Economic depressions still occur, though peaks and valleys in the curve of prosperity may have been made less extreme. Exploitation of the weak brings active retaliation. Man is no longer as willing as he once was to accept with resignation whatever fate may have in store for him.

All this has brought him face to face with the fundamental shortcomings in his own character and that of his fellows. Excessive competition, jealousy, self-centeredness, ruthlessness, psychological manipulation—all these must be dealt with successfully if life is to be endurable (or even possible in this nuclear age). Freud has spoken eloquently of the "hostility to civilization which is produced by the pressure the civilization exercises, the renunciation of instinct which it demands." He then points out that civilization is possible only when we band together to defend ourselves against nature. Unless we do so successfully, "she has her own particularly effective method of restricting us—coldly, cruelly, relentlessly, as it seems to us, and possibly through the very things that occasioned our satisfaction."[2]

This hostility to civilization of which Freud speaks takes many forms, some of them cleverly disguised. In a society that values learning and looks upon books as a means of promoting it, the vandalism now being practiced in our public and college libraries is almost beyond belief. One large urban library has reported thefts amounting to a half million dollars in one year;

the culprits who are caught often profess no feelings of guilt because, as they say, "The books are ours; we paid for them."

Although scenery along the highway is prized by travelers, for many the enjoyment is ruined by ugly billboards or hills barren and disfigured by the strip mining of coal. Thoughtless or rapacious persons endanger the freedoms of speech and press by outrageous offenses against common decency. Rights of privacy are violated without mercy for financial or other personal gain. Far too many of those who are responsible for radio and television programs seem to have no interest in maintaining or elevating standards of taste and behavior but instead exploit the public by spreading broadside their own low sentiments. Christopher Dawson observed, "But our generation has been forced to realize how fragile and unsubstantial are the barriers that separate civilization from the forces of destruction. We have learned that barbarism is not a picturesque myth or half-forgotten memory of a long past stage of history, but an ugly underlying reality which may erupt with shattering force whenever the moral authority of civilization loses its control."[3]

Psychiatrists can engage in prevention of serious mental illness by treating individuals early in the stages of their disorders and mitigating the effects of psychologically noxious influences, and by trying to improve the attitudes of those who are well toward those who are sick. But such efforts are not enough.

Truly effective prevention goes far beyond efforts such as these. It consists of attacking the psychologically harmful influences at all points of origin. Programs of this nature perhaps seem to go beyond the realm of psychiatry even though psychiatrists should have a primary interest in them. It is important that psychiatrists and those who develop community policy be aware of the detrimental influences that interfere with human development, and also of the healthful ones that foster it.

Every child needs love and affection from his parents and other significant persons around him. Feelings of belonging and being wanted are essential to his development and above all to his self-esteem and to his learning self-control. A child needs to be respected by his parents as a separate person, not as an extension of themselves. Firm and consistent discipline from respected people will enable him to establish standards for himself and to recognize what effect his own actions will have on others. He thus becomes able to learn from experience. As he succeeds in little things, he gradually develops a sense of competence as well as the confidence needed in attempting larger tasks. Above all, a child needs good role models on which to pattern himself.

Unfortunately, a reluctance to act on such matters is displayed by many who are in a position to make decisions in individual communities. It is probably due not so much to lack of knowledge about what is theoretically desirable as to a fear that utilization of such knowledge will conflict with prevailing value systems and standards. Strong opinions about individual initiative, co-operation and competition and the relative value of investing in material things rather than in services are not easily changed. Improving conditions for childhood development frequently requires changes in long and firmly held convictions.

A possible remedy for this cherished paralysis of action may well be foreseen in the growing willingness on the part of young people to contribute freely of their time and energy to the grossly underprivileged, both in this country and abroad. The Peace Corps, small as it may be in terms of money expended and tangible results obtained, testifies to a sympathy and respect for others which has heretofore had inadequate channels for expression in action. College students who aid harassed teachers in crowded schools in their neighborhoods, who visit and work in mental hospitals, who engage in special tutoring in settlement houses and who conduct classes in prisons are not only making significant contributions to the welfare of the persons with whom they come in contact, but they are also developing a fundamental, first-hand knowledge of the vast range of contemporary social inequities.

Cooperation seems comparatively easy for man when he is threatened from without by a force which may deprive him of something that he values highly. Wars and other disasters often elicit noble and heroic action. Similarly, when he wants something intensely, he may go to great lengths, even to self-sacrifice, to achieve his ends. Whether his goal is a discovery of a new principle, conquest of nature, elimination of a social injustice, or improvement of a code of conduct, it matters little when individual devotion to a personal cause is involved. What is necessary is that the cause have meaning to him and that his purpose be clear. Whether others understand what he is doing is not immediately relevant. The fact that he is convinced that his work is worthwhile enables him to wait, far into the future if need be, for recognition.

If we continued to have new worlds to conquer, more space into which to expand as the population increases, and external obstacles to surmount we might get along indefinitely with no major changes in our thinking and attitudes, but such is no longer the case. Inner psychological problems demand solution.

Man is now confronted with an awesome choice. He must learn to understand himself and his relations and responsibilities to others, and by this means achieve self-control, or he must resign himself to probable extinction by nuclear weapons or by the slower method of thoughtless and excessive reproduction of his own kind beyond the capacity of his environment to support it. The first choice is an incredibly difficult one to implement, and at present no one knows how to do it; the second choice is easy and may be made by default.

Many of the reasons for man's inability to achieve all of which he is capable have been known to wise men for centuries. But this knowledge has not been applied on a sufficiently wide scale to be universally effective. Small regions of high concentration of scholastic achievement and material progress have appeared here and there—e.g., Ancient China, Egypt, Greece, Italy of the Renaissance, and Elizabethan England. These illustrate the possibilities of human civilization. While these areas of the flowering of civilization may be admirable to us, to persons who have been deprived of their advantages, they may appear in a much less favorable light. Unless the nations and peoples of the world now highly favored with material wealth can understand how they appear to their less affluent, but more numerous, neighbors they will suffer the fate of an organism afflicted with cancer which will grow so fast that it will destroy the entire organism (the world) unless removed by the destructive surgery of war and revolution. A poem by a physician, Dr. John C. Cobb, describes the quandary eloquently:

"Unless we free the spirit of each mind
Disaster haunts abundance for mankind"[4]

By the very nature of his profession, a psychiatrist concentrates his attention on what has gone wrong, on the inappropriate forms of dealing with one's environment, the pathology of the mind. If he is optimistic, it is not because of the nature of his daily work, but because he sees something beyond the tangled and sordid problems with which he deals. What he sees behind the vast assortment of human ills that all too often seem to defy his puny efforts is a set of causes that can be recognized and understood. He believes, almost as a matter of faith, that these basic causes can be eliminated or their harmful effects minimized. He hopes that others will see what he sees and wish to cooperate with him in doing something constructive about improving the human situation.

Anything that diminishes the human spirit is of specific concern to the psychiatrist. Everything that enhances the human spirit is also of interest to him and this concern should be shared by all responsible persons.

I believe that psychiatry as a discipline is just beginning to realize how important human values are to the individual looking for a meaning and purpose in his life. Nearly two centuries ago, the founder of the two Phillips Academies at Exeter and Andover said, "Goodness without knowledge is weak and feeble, yet knowledge without goodness is dangerous; both united form the noblest character and lay the surest foundation of usefulness to mankind."[5] In the intervening period, we have seen many tragic results of failure to recognize this principle. To continue to ignore it will be perilous indeed. Perhaps the time has now come to take these words of wisdom seriously and to use the knowledge we have gained for the betterment of man.

REFERENCES

1. HUGHES, C. C., TREMBLAY, M. A., RAPOPORT, R. N., AND
   LEIGHTON, A. H.: *People of Cove and Woodlot.* New York,
   Basic Books, 1960, pp. 78-89.
2. FREUD, S.: *Standard Edition of Complete Works,* Vol. XXI.
   London, Hogarth Press, 1961, p. 15.
3. DAWSON, C.: *Religion and the Rise of Western Culture.* Garden
   City, Image Books (Doubleday), 1958, p. 24.
4. COBB, J. C.: Letter to the Editor, *Harvard Medical Alumni
   Bulletin,* *38*:2, Spring, 1964.
5. Cited by W. G. Saltonstall, *Life,* March 20, 1964, p. 54.

EPILOGUE

"One of the assets of youth is to feel incomplete, one of the charms of youth is to seem incomplete, and the overwhelming truth about youth is that it is incomplete. . . . It requires no apology . . . for in incompleteness there is promise."

ALAN GREGG

In this volume, I have attempted to portray the ideal role of psychiatry in colleges and universities, what it can and cannot be expected to do, and to suggest the nature of the problems it faces in the years ahead. Ideally, college psychiatrists work to make themselves unnecessary. Their aim is to cooperate with their colleagues in other disciplines to improve the educational process, thereby permitting an increasing number of students to solve their serious problems in the process of growth and development without becoming patients while doing so. The possibility that success might be indefinitely delayed should not obscure the ideal.

Opinions differ as to whether students encounter crippling emotional conflict largely because of environmental factors after entering college or because of disturbances in interpersonal relations in their earlier years. In my opinion, the earlier influences are much more important than the later ones in the development of illness. Conditions in a particular college seldom produce neuroses or psychoses. Students may protest at conditions they dislike, withdraw, or stoically endure unsatisfactory conditions, but something more is needed to produce serious illness. Those who have experienced psychological deficiencies during childhood and early adolescence may be helped to attain emotional maturity by favorable conditions within a college or pushed into disabling illness sooner than

247

otherwise by unfavorable conditions. Hard work and high standards are not of themselves threats to emotional stability.

The problems of students in other countries and cultures have distinguishing features of a superficial nature, but underneath these cultural differences the essential psychological problems are similar all over the world. The various international conferences on student mental health have repeatedly confirmed this opinion.

Thousands of clinical observations support the assumption that parental discord is one of the most important elements in the development of emotional handicaps of children, although as yet incontrovertible scientific proof is lacking. If some parents do a better job of child rearing than others, the differences in their methods should be able to be delineated; subsequently the better methods might be learned and implemented by those interested. One would expect the result to be a higher proportion of children whose development toward emotional maturity was rapid in such families than in those in which the children were unloved, uncared for, and undisciplined. Unfortunately, these assumptions are difficult to prove, and acting on them is neither simple nor easy. A comprehensive research and action program to test the validity of these assumptions should be carried out in a major university, one with superior research personnel and facilities in the social sciences, numerous student families, and students interested in the results. At the least, our students who are soon to become parents, if they are not already, should be helped to make original mistakes in the rearing of their children, rather than those which have been made so often by their parents and grandparents. Teaching college students to become good parents is not a primary function of institutions of higher learning, but furthering this ideal can be encouraged in innumerable ways, direct and indirect, in an institution with many people who appreciate the connections between satisfying family life and the development of responsible intellectual power.

There seems to be a growing apprehension that as the intellectual capacity of our entrants to college becomes greater their emotional problems become more serious. So far as I can learn, no objective evidence has been brought forward to support this point of view. In fact, the preponderant evidence up to now suggests that high intellectual capacity is accompanied by a high degree of emotional stability. As one member of the admissions committee of a college that is highly attractive to prospective students said, "We have not yet refused admission to an applicant because he is intelligent."

A few years ago, while this question was being discussed among admissions committee members at Harvard College, I made a survey of all the students who had sought help from our psychiatric division of the health service the preceding year to discover whether there was any indication of greater usage of the service by those whose scholastic aptitude scores were in the higher ranges. There was none. Clinical evidence suggests that students seek help for disturbances in their interpersonal relations or because of intrapsychic conflicts, and that these are not related to their intellectual capacity but to the nature and quality of the social, cultural, and familial influences under which they grew up.

If I have not already made it clear, I wish now to emphasize certain conclusions that I have drawn from my thirty years of working with students.

College students of the sixties (in the United States) are better informed about their academic subjects, and their fund of general information is better, than students of earlier decades.

Their emotional problems are remarkably similar in character to those displayed by students of the twenties and thirties. There is no solid proof that the incidence of morbidity is any higher now than formerly, but the capacity and willingness to recognize signs of emotional distress and do something to relieve it is much greater now than it was even a few years ago.

The ethical and moral standards of the great majority of college students remain high, probably higher than before World War II, in spite of numerous well publicized lapses of some of them from acceptable behavior. The great majority of students are poorly represented by those who throw over all the conventional values of the past—religious, esthetic, sexual, and moral. Some students engaged in appropriate and even highly desirable

forms of social protest see no distinction between their constructive motives and the extraneous behavior that occasionally
results—fanaticism, intolerance of criticism, and hostility toward
all values held by "the Establishment." With that conspicuous
minority, all the rest of us must be patient until its members have
come to terms with themselves.

Higher education can no longer afford to concentrate on one
aspect of personal development, the intellectual, and assume that
it has no other function than the development of intellectual
power. Power without control is irresponsible and infinitely
dangerous. Emotional stability, thoughtfulness, and concern
with values will enhance, not diminish, intellectual development.

Mental health as a separate concept need not be stressed.
Briefly stated, it entails the capacities or abilities to learn from
experience, acquire satisfaction from constructive achievement,
use leisure time enjoyably and profitably, deal with stresses,
tolerate anxiety, endure frustrations, and exhibit sincerity,
compassion, and humane attitudes.

The basic theoretical framework which guides the work of
most college psychiatrists is psychodynamics, which in turn is
derived in large measure from psychoanalysis. The contributions
to theory made by other divisions of psychology, anthropology,
and sociology are essential. The formulations of Erik Erikson are
known to nearly all college students and must be clearly understood by the psychiatrists who try to help them. No other
theorist, aside from Freud, has been so helpful to college
psychiatrists. The numerous contributors to the understanding
of campus cultures, Nevitt Sanford in particular, have added
immeasurably to our understanding of students. A comprehensive theory of personality development still awaits formulation
and in this task college psychiatrists should do their part.

From its beginning in the United States, higher education has
been dedicated to and dependent upon the preservation of
freedom. Our country's great colleges and universities have led
the fight to resist encroachments upon academic freedom. At
times, adherence to this ideal has required extreme personal
courage and the strength of entire institutions—but the insistence

upon the right to explore the truth has helped maintain the highest of standards. We have now come to realize the necessity of another kind of freedom: the liberation of individuals from those inhibiting forces within themselves which prevent them from achieving their full potential. Educators have long devoted themselves to opposing tyranny of the intellect; now the struggle has been extended, with psychiatrists as allies and colleagues, to include tyranny of emotions. Our goal has become a real freedom of the mind, insofar as that is possible. There have always been limitations, both private and public, but we are in a better position than ever before to help decrease them. College psychiatrists, collaborating with all others in the field of education, may be able, through their efforts to prevent crippling emotional conflict and promote mental health, to help elevate intellectual and ethical standards and also to help students achieve their aspirations.

RECOMMENDED READING

Late Adolescence and Early Adult Development

ACKERMAN, N. W.: *The Psychodynamics of Family Life.* New York, Basic Books, 1958.

ALEXANDER, F.: *Fundamentals of Psychoanaylsis.* New York, Norton, 1948.

ALLPORT, G. W.: *Becoming: Basic Considerations for Psychology.* New Haven, Yale, 1955.

——————: *The Nature of Prejudice.* Cambridge, Beacon Press, 1954.

——————: *Personality and Social Encounter.* Boston, Beacon Press, 1960.

——————: *Patterns in Growth and Personality.* New York, Holt, 1961.

ANGELL, R. C.: *Free Society and Moral Crisis.* Ann Arbor, Univ. of Michigan, 1958.

BALSER, B. H.: *Psychotherapy of the Adolescent.* New York, Internat. Univ. Press, 1957.

BARCLAY, D.: *Understanding the City Child.* New York, Watts, 1959.

BERELSON, B., AND STEINER, G. A.: *Human Behavior: An Inventory of Scientific Findings.* New York, Harcourt, 1964.

BLAINE, G. B., JR., AND MCARTHUR, C. C., Eds.: *Emotional Problems of the Student.* New York, Appleton, 1961.

BLAINE, G. B., JR.: *Patience and Fortitude.* Boston, Little, 1962.

BLOOD, R. O., JR.: *Marriage.* Glencoe, Free Press, 1962.

——————: *New Roles for Men and Women.* New York, Association Press, 1963.

BLOS, P.: *On Adolescence.* Glencoe, Free Press, 1962.

BRACELAND, F. J., AND STOCK, M.: *Modern Psychiatry—A Handbook for Believers.* New York, Doubleday, 1963.

CALDERONE, M. S.: *Release from Sexual Tensions.* New York, Random, 1960.

CAPLAN, G.: *An Approach to Community Mental Health.* New York, Grune and Stratton, 1961.

CHEIN, I., *et al.*: *The Road to H—Narcotics, Delinquency and Social Policy*. New York, Basic Books, 1964.

CLARK, J. A., Ed.: *The Student Seeks an Answer*. Waterville, Colby College Press, 1960.

CRAWLEY, L. Q., MALFETTI, J. L., STEWARD, E. I., AND DIAS, N. V.: *Reproduction, Sex, and Preparation for Marriage*. Englewood Cliffs, Prentice-Hall, 1964.

DAVIS, M.: *Sexual Responsibility in Marriage*. New York, Dial Press, 1963.

DE SMIT, B. N. W.: *From Person into Patient*. The Hague, Paris and Morton, 1963.

DONHAM, W. B.: *Education for Responsible Living*. Cambridge, Harvard, 1944.

EDDY, E. D., JR., PARKHURST, M. L., AND YAKOVAKIS, J. S.: *The College Influence on Student Character*. Washington, D. C., Amer. Council Education, 1959.

ERIKSON, E. H.: Young Man Luther. New York, Norton, 1958.

—————: *Identity and the Life Cycle, Selected Papers, Psychological Issues*, 1:1. New York, Internat. Univ. Press, 1959.

—————: *Childhood and Society*. 2nd Ed. New York, Norton, 1963.

—————, Ed.: *Youth: Change and Challenge*. New York, Basic Books, 1963.

—————: *Insight and Responsibility*. New York, Norton, 1964.

FARBER, S. M., AND WILSON, R. H. L.: *Control of the Mind*. New York, McGraw-Hill, 1961.

FARBEROW, N. L., AND SCHNEIDMAN, E. S.: *The Cry for Help*. New York, McGraw-Hill, 1961.

FARNSWORTH, D. L.: *Mental Health in College and University*. Cambridge, Harvard, 1957.

—————, Ed.: *College Health Administration*. New York, Appleton, 1964.

—————: *College Health Services in the United States*. Washington, American College Personnel Association (a Division of American Personnel and Guidance Assoc.), 1965.

FISHBEIN, M., AND BURGESS, E. W.: *Successful Marriage*. Rev. Ed. New York, Doubleday, 1955.

FRANKEL, C., Ed.: *Issues in University Education*. New York, Harper, 1959.

FREUD, S.: *Outline of Psychoanalysis*. New York, Norton, 1949.

——————: *Collected Papers* (5 Vols.). New York, Basic Books, 1959.

FRIEDENBERGER, E. Z.: *The Vanishing Adolescent*. Boston, Beacon Press, 1959.

FRY, C. C.: *Mental Health in College*. New York, Commonwealth Fund, 1942.

FUNKENSTEIN, D. H., Ed.: *The Student and Mental Health—An International View*. New York, World Federation for Mental Health (124 E. 28th St.), 1959.

GALLAGHER, J. R., AND HARRIS, H. I.: *Emotional Problems of Adolescents*. 2nd Ed. New York, Oxford, 1964.

GARDNER, J. W.: *Excellence*. New York, Harper, 1961.

——————: *Self-Renewal—The Individual and the Innovative Society*. New York, Harper, 1964.

GARRISON, R.: *The Adventure of Learning in College*. New York, Harper, 1959.

GASSERT, R. G., AND HALL, B. H.: *Psychiatry and Religious Faith*. New York, Viking, 1964.

GINZBERG, E., AND FARDNER, J. W.: *Values and Ideals of American Youth*. New York, Columbia Univ. Press, 1961.

GOLDSEN, R. K., *et al.*: *What College Students Think*. New York, Van Nostrand, 1960.

GRINDER, R. E., Ed.: *Studies in Adolescence*. New York, Macmillan, 1963.

G.A.P. REPORT No. 17: *The Role of Psychiatrists in Colleges and Universities*. New York (104 E. 25th St., New York 10010), Revised January 1957.

G.A.P. REPORT No. 32: *Considerations on Personality Development in College Students*. New York, May 1955.

G.A.P. REPORT No. 52: *The College Experience*: *A Focus for Psychiatric Research*. New York, May 1962.

G.A.P. REPORT No. 60: *Sex and the College Student*. New York, 1965.

HARMS, E., Ed.: *Drug Addiction in Youth*. New York, Pergamon Press, 1965.

HEIN, F. V., AND FARNSWORTH, D. L.: *Living*. 4th Ed. Chicago, Scott, Foresman, 1965.

HOLMES, D. J.: *The Adolescent in Psychotherapy*. Boston, Little, 1964.

JACOB, P. E.: *Changing Values in College*. New York, Harper, 1957.

JAHODA, M.: *Current Concepts of Positive Mental Health*. New York, Basic Books, 1958.

JERSILD, A. T.: *The Psychology of Adolescence.* New York Macmillan, 1957.

JOHNSON, E. W.: *Love and Sex in Plain Language.* Philadelphia, Lippincott, 1965.

JOINT COMMISSION ON MENTAL ILLNESS AND HEALTH: *Action for Mental Health.* New York, Basic Books, 1961.

JOSSELYN, I. M.: *The Adolescent and His World.* New York, Family Service Assoc. of America, 1952.

——————: *The Happy Child.* New York, Random, 1955.

KING, S. H.: *Perceptions of Illness and Medical Practice.* New York, Russell Sage Foundation, 1962.

KIRKENDALL, L. A.: *Premarital Intercourse and Interpersonal Relationships.* New York, Julian Press, 1961.

KLUCKHOLN, C., MURRAY, H. A., AND SCHNEIDER, D. M., Eds.: *Personality in Nature, Society and Culture.* 2nd Ed. New York, Knopf, 1953.

LEVY, J., AND MUNROE, R.: *The Happy Family.* New York, Knopf, 1938.

LIFTON, R. J.: *Thought Reform and the Psychology of Totalism.* New York, Norton, 1961.

LIPPMAN, H. S.: *Treatment of the Child in Emotional Conflict.* 2nd Ed. New York, McGraw-Hill, 1962.

LIPSET, S. M., AND LOWENTHAL, L.: *Culture and Social Character.* Glencoe, Free Press, 1961.

McGARTHY, R. G., Ed.: *Drinking and Intoxication.* Glencoe, Free Press, 1959.

MENNINGER, K. A.: *The Vital Balance.* New York, Viking, 1963.

MUDD, E. H., AND KRICH, A.: *Man and Wife.* New York, Basic Books, 1957.

MURPHY, G.: *Human Potentialities.* New York, Basic Books, 1958.

MURPHY, L. B., AND RAUSHENBUSH, E., Eds.: *Achievement in the College Years.* New York, Harper, 1960.

NIXON, R. E.: *The Art of Growing.* New York, Random, 1962.

PARKER, E.: *The Seven Ages of Woman.* Baltimore, Johns Hopkins Press, 1960.

PEARSON, G. H. J.: *Adolescence and the Conflict of Generations.* New York, Norton, 1958.

PEPINSKY, H. B., AND PEPINSKY, P. N.: *Counseling, Theory and Practice.* New York, Ronald, 1954.

PORTER, R. H.: *An Introduction to Therapeutic Counseling.* Boston Houghton, 1950.

PRESCOTT, D. A.: *The Child in the Educative Process.* New York, McGraw-Hill, 1957.

RAUSHENBUSH, E.: *The Student and His Studies.* Middletown, Wesleyan Univ. Press, 1964.

RIDENOUR, N.: *Mental Health in the United States.* Cambridge, Harvard, 1961.

RIESMAN, D.: *The Lonely Crowd.* New Haven, Yale, 1950.

——————: *Individualism Reconsidered.* Glencoe, Free Press, 1954.

——————: *Contraint and Variety in American Education.* Lincoln, Univ. Nebraska Press, 1956.

——————: *Abundance for What?* New York, Doubleday, 1964.

RIESMAN, D., JACOB, P. E., AND SANFORD, N.: *Spotlight on the College Student.* Washington, D. C., Amer. Council Education, 1959.

SANFORD, N., Ed.: *The American College.* New York, Wiley, 1962.

——————, Ed.: *College and Character.* New York, Wiley, 1964.

SAUL, L. J.: *Bases of Human Behavior.* Philadelphia, Lippincott, 1951.

——————: *The Hostile Mind.* New York, Random, 1956.

——————: *Emotional Maturity.* 2nd Ed. Philadelphia, Lippincott, 1960.

SEARS, R. R., MACCOBY, E. E., AND LEVIN, H.: *Patterns of Child Rearing.* Evanston, Row, Peterson, 1957.

SHNEIDMAN, E. S., AND FARBEROW, N. L.: *Clues to Suicide.* New York, McGraw-Hill, 1957.

STEVENSON, G. S.: *Mental Health Planning for Social Action.* New York, McGraw-Hill, 1956.

SUTHERLAND, R. L., et al., Eds.: *Personality Factors on the College Campus.* Austin, Texas, Hogg Foundation for Mental Health, 1962.

TYLER, L. E.: *The Work of the Counselor.* 2nd Ed. New York, Appleton, 1961.

UHR, L., AND MILLER, J. G., Eds.: *Drugs and Behavior.* New York, Wiley, 1960.

WALTER, E. A., Ed.: *Religion and the State University.* Ann Arbor, Univ. Michigan Press, 1958.

WEDGE, B. M., Ed.: *Psychosocial Problems of College Men.* New Haven, Yale, 1958.

WHEELIS, A.: *The Quest for Identity.* New York, Norton, 1958.

WHITTINGTON, H. G.: *Psychiatry on the College Campus.* New York, Internat. Univ. Press, 1963.

WILLIAMS, E.: *Vocational Counseling.* New York, McGraw-Hill, 1965.

WITMER, H. L., AND KOTINSKY, R.: *Personality in the Making.* New York, Harper, 1952.

ZILBOORG, G.: *Psychoanalysis and Religion.* New York, Farrar, Straus and Cudahy, 1962.

INDEX

A

Abortions, 153
  research on effects of, 211
Academic performace, prediction of, 208
Acting out, 33-34, 216
Action for Mental Health, 9
Addiction, definition of, 109
  incidence of, 111
  reasons for, 111
Administrative studies, of college students, 203-204
Admissions office, 11
  and health information, 193
Adolescence, characteristics of, 30-33
  controls in, 34
Alcohol, college regulations on, 118
  in U.S., use of, 116-117
Alcoholism, definition of, 117
  incidence in college, 117
  prevention of, 118
American College Health Association, 5, 210
American Medical Association, 10, 131
  statement on mental illness, 214
American Psychiatric Association, 10
Amorality, 157
Amphetamine, characteristics of, 114-115
  false assumptions about, 115
Anti-intellectualism, 226
Apathy, 54-58
Appel, Kenneth, 10
Arbuckle, Dugald S., 166
Arnstein, Robert L., on dropouts, 98
Asher, Harry, on hallucinogens, 126
Attrition (*see* Dropouts)
Authority, attitudes toward, 146

dealing with, 38-40
Automation, 135

B

Balser, Benjamin H., on prediction of mental disturbances, 208
Balser, Paula B., 213
Barbiturates, 113
Barger, Ben, 48
Barzun, Jacques, 27
Becker, Paul, 27
Beecher, Henry K., 127
  on amphetamine effects, 114-115
Behavioral changes, as sign of emotional conflict, 58
"Bennies," 114
Benzedrine, 114
Bennett, Chester C., on hallucinogens, 131
Berelson, Bernard R., 203
Berkeley (*see* California, University of)
"Bhang," 111
Bidwell, Charles, 232
Blaine, Graham B., Jr., on divided loyalties, 194n
Blanton, Smiley, 3
Bond, Earl D., 15
Bordin, Edward S., 166
Brief psychotherapy, 211, 217, 225
Brown, J. B., study of pregnant unmarried women, 165
Bruyn, Henry B., on sex behavior, 152
  on suicide, 85-86
Bureau of Study Counsel, 200

C

Caffeine, 115

259

Tyler, Leona E., on counseling, 166
Tyranny of emotions, 250

U

Undergraduates, attitude toward
  student-teachers, 137-138
Universities, and bigness, 140
Urban, Hugh B., on dropouts, 97-98,
  101
U.S. Public Health Service, 121
U.S. Supreme Court, and Bill of
  Rights, 190

V

Values, 228-235
  conflicts in, 224
  contrasts in, effects of, 43, 95, 102
  contribution of college to, 183, 185
  definition of, 229
  and ethics, 145
  origins of, 45
  transmission of, 144-146, 229-235
  trend toward mediocrity, 45
Vandalism, 33
  in libraries, 19, 241
Vassar College, 3
von Stade, F. Skiddy, Jr., 5
Voyeurism, 155
Vreeland, Rebecca, 232
Vulnerability to stress, reduction of,
  220-222

W

Wacker, Ernest A., 213
Walters, Paul A., Jr., on apathy, 54
Washburn College, 3
Wasson, R. Gordon, on hallucinogens,
  124
Wedge, Bryant M., 167
Wheelright, Joseph B., on suicide, 87
Whitehead, Alfred N., on education,
  185
Whitehorn, John C., 27
Wilkie, George H., 186
Williamson, Edward G., on counseling,
  166
Wilms, John H., 21
Wilson, Roger H. L., 131
Wisconsin, University of, 3
Women students, problems of, 80-81
  (see also Pregnancy)

Y

Yale University, 3
  dropout rate of, 98
  psychoses study, 52
  suicide study, 87
"Yellow jackets," 113

Z

Zilboorg, Gregory, on Freud and
  religion, 230

Lectures Published in This Series